Melanie Dale has written a book that I wish I had nine years ago when I was wallowing in the depths of infertility while my über-fertile friends made babies with gumball machine efficiency. I would've given my left ovary (I said, "It looks like the Death Star!" during my ultrasound) to have had this book, or a friend like her, at that time. If you're going through infertility, read this book and take heart. There are lots of us out there who have felt like you do now, and Melanie put it all on paper. With lots of amazing Nerd references, both the candy and pop-culture types.

Jeanette Strole Parks, *former published indie music critic and occasional food/home improvement blogger. Adoptive mother of one, after nine years of infertility. Olympia, Washington.*

Infreakinfertility is a book I wish I would have had when I was in the trenches of infertility. Melanie shares her journey through infertility with the perfect combination of vulnerability, humor, and practical advice. She gives us an authentic glimpse of what it is like to walk this difficult road and guidance to keep taking the next step forward.

Hope Dover, *freelance writer, wife, mother of four – two babies in heaven and a son and daughter here – struggled with endometriosis, infertility, and pregnancy loss. York, South Carolina.*

This is your "I'm not the only one" and "this stinks for everyone" book. If you are dealing with infertility this book will be a confirmation that you are not alone, or crazy. If you know someone dealing with infertility, read this so you can know how to be the perfect friend, not "that" friend. Everyone will be better off for it.

Amy Tilson, *wife, adoptive momma, and survivor of four IVFs, serial mover, and world changer. Reston, Virginia.*

If you are struggling with infertility and think no one understands, think again. Melanie and her husband relate their story in a humorous and understanding way. You will definitely not feel alone after reading their story!

Jerralea Miller, *blogger, ministry assistant, mother of three who walked through ten years of infertility, and now MiMi of three. Tamms, Illinois.*

Melanie has done it again! When I was knee deep in my fertility journey and read *It's Not Fair*, I had no idea it would affect me so profoundly and change the shape of my journey through infertility simply by making me feel seen and validated in my pain. If *It's Not Fair* did that, *Infreakinfertility* carries on in that spirit but hits with even more precision. With her No-Holds-Barred approach, Melanie touches on every aspect of surviving the devastation of infertility, from the emotional/spiritual side, to the relational side, to the physical/medical side, to sex! And all while making me laugh out loud. I'm so grateful!

> **Leah Kelton**, *photographer & graphic designer at Whispers of Light Photography & Design, author in the making who blogs at www.godkindled.com, and ecstatic mother-to-be (FINALLY!). Buckinghamshire, United Kingdom.*

Infertility sucks, we all know it, but not everyone talks about it. Some people avoid the subject, not wanting to cause discomfort, some people talk about it too openly without knowing that their words meant for encouragement actually hurt us more, and there are those who are oblivious. Melanie has a way of inviting you into her story, laying it on the table for all to see, yet making you feel heard, too. I felt like she was able to speak some of the words written on my heart that I am too bashful or scared to say out loud or put in writing. She gives weight to areas that others forget or don't see and reminds us that we are not what we go through. We are refined by our experiences, made stronger and wiser, not defined by them. Trials will come, life was never supposed to be easy, but knowing other people are going through the same thing makes life a little bit easier. Thanks to Melanie for her bravery and honesty and of course for the doodles and humor.

> **Katie King Rumford**, *graphic designer, wife of a rockstar (not literally, but I'm his number one fan), sister to five incredible brothers, dog mom, IVF survivor, and a hopeful yet-to-be-mother. Dana Point, California.*

Melanie brings empathy (and at times hilarity) to a desperately rough experience. If you are going through infertility, *Infreakinfertility* will help you realize you are not alone and what you are feeling is normal. This book is a must read for anyone whose life has been touched, directly or indirectly, by infertility.

> **Jennifer Weston**, *wife, chemist, photographer, cat lover, Diet Coke drinker, and loving life with no children. Julian, Pennsylvania.*

Melanie has found a way to write a book about infertility that doesn't leave you feeling overwhelmed or bored by hearing the same old thing. She takes common experiences, thoughts, and feelings and explores those ideas in fresh ways. Her humor makes you laugh, but doesn't discredit how hard infertility is. She isn't afraid to tackle hard and awkward topics. I appreciated her ability to write in such an authentic way.

   Heather McDonald, *teacher, mother, survivor of infertility after miscarriage. Knoxville, Tennessee.*

If my ovaries had a cheer squad, Melanie Dale would be cheer captain and win the spirit stick. She takes a delicate topic that most feel is off limits and manages to weave humor and practical application into one awesome read. If you are experiencing infertility or know someone who is, this book lets you know that you are not alone.

   Ginny Starr, *co-founder of Forever We, mom of two. Atlanta, Georgia.*

In her usual style, Melanie tackles the difficult topic of infertility with boldness and humor. If you are looking for a book that screams "ME TOO," then this is it. Through all my years of infertility struggles, I never had a book that made me feel sane or that echoed so much of what I felt. I wish I had this book to make me feel less alone at that time. Not only will you shout a lot of "amens" as you read it, but you will also laugh and cry. And you will appreciate having a male perspective as Melanie's husband shares in each chapter. This book is practical and should be given to every woman you know because either she is facing infertility or knows someone who is. If you aren't infertile, then read this book to better understand how to help your friend who is because it says all the things she may be scared to say to you.

   Jenny Jerkins, *Jesus freak, wife, mom through domestic infant adoption. Augusta, Georgia.*

Infreakinfertility is a "bare all" guide to every aspect of infertility. Melanie invites women and couples in all stages of infertility to peek in to her experience and offers real, practical tips on how to survive. Her journey and anecdotes will make you laugh-cry in the best way possible. A must-read for those struggling with or caring for someone dealing with infertility.

   Kristy Blouin, *Christian, wife, and mother of two after seven years of primary and secondary infertility. Tampa, Florida.*

infreakinfertility

infreakinfertility

How to Survive
When Getting Pregnant
Gets Hard

melanie dale

UNEXPECTED MEDIA

Infreakinfertility
Copyright © 2018 by Melanie Dale
melanie@unexpected.org

This title is also available in ebook format.

Requests for information should be addressed to:
Unexpected Media, PO Box 3410, Peachtree City, GA 30269
www.unexpected.org

ISBN 978-0-692-19017-3

Cover Design: Alex Dale
Interior Illustration: Melanie Dale
Interior Design: Alex Dale
Author Photo: Donna Page

To the makers of home pregnancy tests.
May your pee always burn and smell like asparagus.

TABLE OF CONTENTS

INTRO-
DUCTION

"When are you going to have kids?"

Fletch: "Well, there we're in kind of a grey area."
Frank Walker: "How grey?"
Fletch: "Charcoal."
–Fletch

My uterus makes me so mad.

In a world where people's sexy parts routinely come together to carry on the human race with the clockwork and precision of little Army recruits, my uterus flits around like a Boho flower child making its own magic and not letting anyone be the boss of it. I plead with it to be like the other uteruses and fall in line, but it refuses, clenching its fist in crampy insolence.

About a minute after finding the love of your life, people start asking when you're going to have kids. As a society, mating is really important to us, and depending on what your family is like, it can kind of feel like a group project. And if you say you're trying, a countdown begins and the longer it goes on with no news, the more pressure you feel.

There are these conversations that happen in secret, behind closed doors or squeezed into back pews of churches or on living room floors when no one else is home. We are the infertile ones, pasting on smiles in public and asking hard questions into the silence. We're cast out of the established pattern for families, and we seek solace and solidarity in a world meant for being fruitful and multiplying.

We feel like freaks. About being freakin' infertile. And the freakishness must end. But it's hard to talk about. I'll go first. I'll tell you all the private things and will keep talking until no one is suffering in silence.

This is kind of a big deal to me, because not so many years ago I contemplated killing myself over the babylessness. I don't want you to get to that point. And while I hope that every infertile person in the world has a nice infertile mentor helping her walk through this, like Yoda and Luke Skywalker training together in the Dagoba System, I keep hearing from

people who feel alone. I don't want you to feel alone, so I'll be your grumpy Yoda, albeit clumsier and slightly taller. I'd say my skill with a light saber is marginal at best. (That's a penis joke.)

This isn't a book about conquering infertility. This is a book about surviving it.

This is not a book about what's okay and what's not okay in the world of fertility treatments. When I research infertility, I keep finding a lot about ethics and not very much about coping and feelings and relationships and caring for yourself. A whole lot of people have opinions about our uteruses and vaginas, and that makes me really sad. At least buy me dinner first before deciding how to knock me up.

So this isn't a book about what is and isn't okay. I might mention a procedure that we didn't want to do and you might be uncomfortable with something we totally embraced. We all have to make these choices in what I believe is a grey area. This book is about freedom, not judgment. If you tell me you drizzled your belly with pig's blood and sang the national anthem I will not judge you. I will just hug you. These are desperate

ME:
BABY—
LESS
FREAK

times and we're all a little strung out and just trying to make the right decisions. Love.

This is also not a book about science, although I'm going to talk about fertility treatments. But I went through that a decade ago and I sure do hope the big-brained scientists have made at least a few advancements since then. So if you're looking for the latest scientific specifics, head to your doctor or The Google.

In the *Harry Potter* series, J.K. Rowling calls non-magical people "muggles," and I think for our purposes here, we need a name for fertile people. We love them, they mean well, and we're surrounded by them, but in some ways, they cannot understand our secret society of infertility. I've heard people refer to them as "breeders," but that makes me think of an alien life form laying egg sacs in people's brains in order to take over the human race. I may spend an inordinate amount of time thinking about alien egg sacs.

Let's refer to our fertile brethren as "Fertles." I was going to spell this with a "u," but Urban Dictionary's number one definition for "furtle" is a sex tourist in Southeast Asia.[1] So let's go with "Fertle" with an "e," because when it comes to sex tourism in any part of the world, I'm rather against it. My own attempted procreating sexcapades are exhausting enough without adding long flights, strangers, and crime.

FERTLE
NOT
FURTLE
SEX
TOURIST

---

[1] http://www.urbandictionary.com/define.php?term=furtle

Hey, Fertles, if you're reading this, thanks for being such good friends and family members to your infertile loved ones. Hopefully this book will help you figure out how to support them better. (My friends going through infertility, I'll teach you the secret handshake at our next clandestine meeting.)

If you're experiencing infertility then you get to figure out what to do and how to survive and which choices to make, and I want to walk with you through that. I've gone through it, so I will tell you all about what we did and how we coped and some things that helped. By the time this book is published, the good scientists may have figured out how to launch a mini rocket ship of embryos directly into your endometrial lining while you practice *ujjayi* breathing in downward facing dog. There could be sperm spaceships impregnating women while flossing. I cannot know these things. This could be the book you read while waiting for your vaginal rocket. We are living in a golden age.

Full disclosure: I have kids. I don't even want to tell you that in case it hurts you more, living in a world where flipping everyone has kids. I went through phases during my struggle with infertility. Some days other people getting pregnant gave me hope, and some days it gave me rage hives. So I'm sorry for your rage hives. My first child was born through in vitro fertilization after a five-year battle with infertility. Elliott was our one and only successful attempt of all the attempts with all the different ways. This book will mostly be about our road to him, but I'll also spend a little bit of ink on my daughters. We adopted our youngest, Evie, from Ethiopia as a toddler and she is nobody's plan B backup baby, let me tell you. Evie, if you're reading this, Mommy's infertility was so awful and I hate that it happened, but you, you my dear, are the greatest gift. And we adopted Ana, our oldest, from Latvia when she was nine, and she is also the greatest gift. And so is Elliott. Kids, all three of you are tied for greatest gift ever, so no need to go all *Gladiator* on each other and fight to the death, mkay? Greatest gifts, in all the different ways you came to us.

Despite having three whole kids, I'm still a barren wasteland. My uterus is like the desert planet of Tatooine (yes, I know that's two *Star Wars* references and we're still in the introduction). I have endometriosis and can't get pregnant naturally, even when standing on my head after sex. So, I have three kids, am still infertile, but am no longer trying to make human beings with my body.

Infertile couples are longing for people who understand, don't judge them, and have experience in this area. As I've shared bits of my stories with my friends, in my previous books, and online, I've had many women reach out with their own stories and questions. I offer this book to all the couples out there who need to hear they aren't alone.

This is my attempt to write the book I wish I'd had when I was going through infertile hell. It's for women, it's for couples, and my husband, Alex, is going to share his perspective throughout the book. Pretend like we've invited you over for dinner. We're opening up our home, offering our own experience, and trying to answer your questions. We are not doctors, theologians, or philosophers, so we're not offering medical or ethical advice. We're just a regular couple like you who tried to survive and figure out what to do when faced with a terrible situation.

I kept trying to find people to talk to when we were in the thick of decision-making agony, and we found one family whose kids were all made through in vitro. I watched her nurse twins at the same time and asked her all my questions. This is like that, except I don't have twins and my kids are older and the thought of nursing them now makes me want to throw up.

I've organized this book by stupid things people said to me. Some of them are incredibly stupid and should win some kind of idiot award, and some are perfectly normal but I wanted to yell "YOU STUPIDHEAD" at the time, even though

We feel like freaks. About being freakin' infertile. And the freakishness must end.

they were lovely people and didn't deserve such treatment.

Each chapter deals with a different challenge with infertility and is broken into sections, a little of my story and concerns, a blurb from Alex about his thoughts from the male perspective, and practical tips on how to cope. My goal is that throughout this book you will feel heard and seen, that you'll feel like you aren't alone, that you can use our experience to explain infertility to the people pressing around you, or just hand this book to them if you don't have the emotional energy, and that you'll learn some tips to help you through this difficult time.

Let's get started.

TRYING

"You just need to relax."

Yoda: "Do. Or do not. There is no try."
-*The Empire Strikes Back*

Yoda's wrong. There is try, and it is a particularly debilitating phase of infertile purgatory.

Raise your hand if someone told you to "just relax" in the last month. In the last week. Today. How many times today has someone told you that? "You just need to relax." You're like, "I'm trying to relax but everyone keeps telling me to relax which is making me tense."

How do you relax when the thing you want so badly is eluding you month in, month out and you are powerless to make it happen? We tried relaxing. I took my mind off getting pregnant, got excited about other things, refocused. Months later, still no baby. I made good grades in school, got into the college where I wanted to go, never really had a major

thing that I couldn't achieve without hard work and diligence. Until infertility. I could not work my way out of it. I could not make myself get pregnant.

At first you think nothing of it. You've seen the films with the egg and sperm and know sometimes it takes a few tries for the swimmers to wiggle in the right direction. But after a while, you start to have that growing suspicion that making a baby is harder than you thought and you begin to use the "i" word with trepidation...infertility. The first time you say it out loud feels weird. You talk to a friend and say it out loud. "I'm worried we're struggling with infertility."

Family members start whispering about you with hushed tones, tilting their heads to the

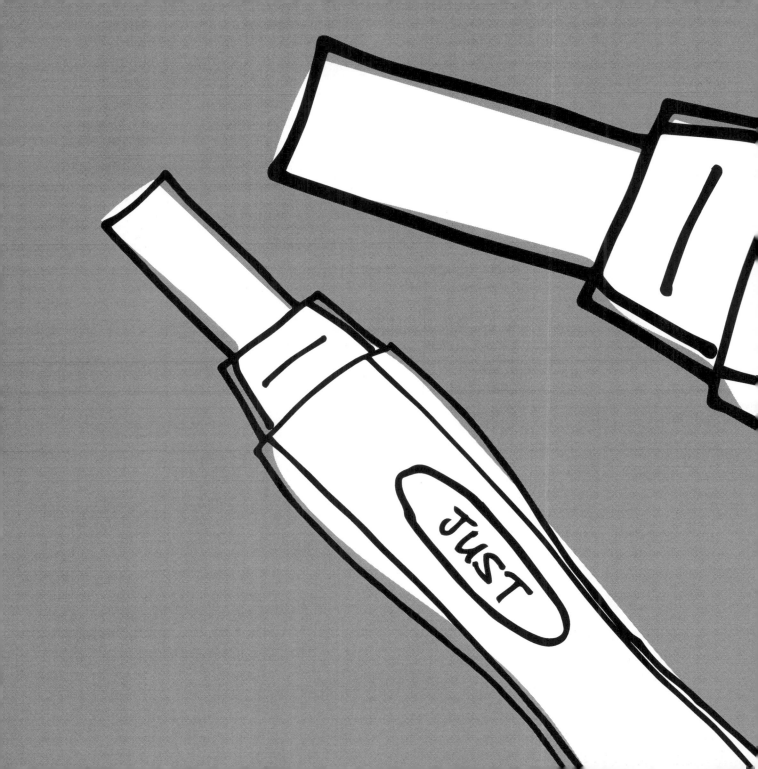

side and asking how you're holding up. Some joke about how "at least it's fun trying." Yep, there's nothing like the rush of trying to achieve orgasm at the exact moment your fallopian tube drops that tender egg into your uterus. Nothing turns me on like being afraid to move in case I disturb a newly formed embryo from bedding down in my endometrial lining. Nothing turns my husband on like thinking about my fluffy endometrial lining.

But we made the best of it, and I'm sure you did, too.

You experience a series of emotions throughout your journey with infertility. Maybe some of these are familiar to you.

"I'm fine."

People ask how you're doing, you respond, "I'm fine," and you convince yourself that this is true. You are totally holding it together and are okay either way this pee stick goes. Whether it has one line or two, shows "blue" or not, or if you spring for the expensive ones, actually comes out and tells you "pregnant" or "not pregnant," you will rise above your feelings and soldier on. Why grieve when you live in a world with Netflix and avocado toast? Everything is fine, baby or not.

"This is better."

You're not just fine with no baby, you're happy about it. You thought you really wanted to get pregnant, but now that you've tried it a bunch and it didn't work out, you've realized this is perfect. You'll buckle down at work, apply for that promotion, finally read all that Russian lit you meant to get to after college, and sign up to raft the Grand Canyon.

"Now I can travel."

That's right. Now that a baby isn't holding you back, you can travel. You and your partner can renew your passports, manscape that back hair, and head off to Belize for a much-needed vacay. What were you thinking? Instead of packing a diaper bag, you're packing a bikini and heading out into the world to make memories.

The Dory: "Just Keep Swimming"

Okay, maybe you're slightly bummed about still not being pregnant. When your sister called you to share some "big news" you made the appropriate *squeeee* noises but for some weird reason your finger kept shooting her the bird through the phone. Bad, finger, bad. Where is this aggression coming from? Everything is still fine, and you just need to keep swimming, like an elite fleet of healthy sperm.

"Life is over."

Cue the Eric Carmen power ballad. You are all by yourself. Another month lost. This is never going to happen and you're going to end up old and alone with no one to change your Depends.

Maybe you're actively peeing on sticks to determine exactly when you're ovulating, or maybe you're keeping a calendar or having sex every other day just to be thorough. You are trying. You are trying so hard. And you're trying to keep it light and fun because you're trying to relax while trying.

Good job. You get an A+ for effort.

If you've been trying long enough that the people around you have noticed and someone put this book in your hands, let me tell you right now, it's not your fault. It's not your fault that you aren't pregnant yet. You're trying just as hard as other people, probably harder. If you're like me, it's tempting to blame yourself or your partner or both.

I blamed myself for not relaxing enough, for not having enough sex or having it at the wrong time, for the experimental acne medication I took in high school, for the raging eating disorder, and for not being able to overcome my genetic disposition. And for using lotions with parabens. The parabens were the culprit for sure. And growing up on Velveeta and Hot Pockets and too much BPA in all the canned foods we ate in the '80s before farmers' markets were a thing we did in the suburbs.

Plenty of blame running around in my head and maybe you're struggling with that, too. But you know what? People have been getting randomly pregnant in spite of history, lifestyle, and timing for millennia, so let's let ourselves off the hook on this one, okay? It's not your fault. Stop trying to argue with me. It's not.

THINGS TO BLAME

- [ ] PARABENS
- [x] BPA
- [ ] GOD
- [x] STUPID GENETICS
- [ ] TOO MANY HOT POCKETS
- [ ] SOYLENT GREEN

Powerless

"Be strong for Melanie." I used to coach myself with these words. But as months of trying turned into years, my optimism was running thin. My encouraging remarks seemed hollow and overplayed.

We were finally ready for kids. The requisite "getting-to-know-each-other" part of marriage was over. Now it was time to move on to babies and soccer games and daddy-daughter date nights. We had a plan, but the more time went by, the more I could feel it slipping through my fingers.

What's more, I felt powerless to help my wife – like watching a car accident in slow motion. Her depression was insidious, slowly stripping away her joy. And I felt like I couldn't do anything to fix it.

When I was twenty-three, I got fired from my job. It was debilitating. I went on almost thirty interviews in the course of two months. Very little Melanie said comforted me. I was engaged to be married, but I was worried I wouldn't be able to provide for my wife. I felt defeated, lost, and alone.

Infertility kicked me in the gut. But it came nowhere close to how my wife felt. I truly didn't understand Melanie's feelings until she compared her inability to get pregnant with the inadequacy I felt losing my job. Her innate sense of purpose was being attacked, and it was tearing her apart.

5 Tips for Trying

01 Manage your expectations when you start trying to get pregnant. I totally thought I'd get pregnant the first month I went off the pill, like my eggs had just been waiting for me to take the handcuffs off.

02 Commit to an agreed-upon timetable with your partner before you start thinking about getting help. For example, maybe you decide together that you'll try for six months or a year before making a call.

03 Don't tell anyone you're trying unless you're okay with that person checking in about it. Everyone has a different tolerance level for other people poking around his or her life. You might be fine with your families, your coworkers, and all your neighbors asking about your ovulation, but your spouse might want to lock it down until there's something to share. Have that conversation and get on the same page before opening up to other people. This could be a long road and you need to think about who you want traveling on that road with you for the duration.

When you're experiencing infertility, you can feel like everyone in the tri-state area is aware of your cycle, sperm count, and whether or not you're able to perform sexually. You feel exposed for everyone to see. People add you to prayer lists and lay their hands on your empty womb (awkward) and your "failure" and "brokenness" is extremely obvious. Once you tell people that you're trying to conceive...and then don't... your struggle is extremely public. There's no way to cover up a lack of baby. Everyone has an opinion on every decision, and you can feel like you have to justify your choices.

It's a tricky balance, because if you choose to keep quiet about infertility and not tell anyone what you're going through, then you're still stuck with the "when are you going to have kids?" questions, and also you're walking alone through one of the hardest things you've ever faced. You and your partner have each other, but that can put a real strain on a relationship when you're expected to manage all of each other's fears and freakouts, questions and feelings.

So if you don't tell everyone, maybe you at least tell someone, a trusted friend or therapist, someone who can check in with you and listen while you process everything.

I told everyone, because that's just my way. I mean, I'm writing a whole book about it, so whatever. The only thing I regret about that is feeling like everyone's project to solve. I couldn't even show up at family vacations without people wanting to talk with me about it. There was no escaping.

04 **Start a journal.** If you like to write, this could be a long-winded tirade of your feelings, but it could also be one sentence a day or a bulleted list. Start tracking how you're feeling, things you notice about your body, sex, time with your partner. If faith is a component of your life, maybe you jot a prayer every now and then. A journal is a great place to vent if you are trying

to minimize the number of people you're telling.

05 **Give it a few months before you panic**, but don't wait so long that you're a total basket case by the time you call the doctor. We waited too long. I just kept thinking, "Well, maybe we missed the window for my ovulating again. We could've had better timing." And people kept telling me I'm so young! I have time! Because of how young I am! That should've been my first clue that something was wrong, though, because my eggs were fresh as the Prince of Bel-Air. On the flip side, I had an acquaintance who freaked out after one month of trying. At that point I was at four years and counting, so I may have struggled to sympathize when her dreams didn't come true after one month.

After you try for the amount of time you'd planned on trying, whether it's six months or a year or another number, and you're still not pregnant, you have some decisions to make together. For some people, fertility treatments are not an option, whether for religious convictions, financial constraints, or other reasons. If that's you, total respect, feel free to skip the next chapter and judge me all you want. For others, everything is on the table and they want to try, and can afford to try, whatever it takes. For a lot of us, we find ourselves somewhere in the middle, where we're looking for what our options are, how much they'll cost, what the statistics are for success, what kind of toll it's going to take on our bodies and wallets, and then deciding a path. Let's talk about the path.

Oz.

SEEKING HELP

"My boss's wife's massage therapist knows a guy."

Monica: "I can't believe this. My uterus is an inhospitable environment? I've always tried so hard to be a good hostess!"
–Friends

Somewhere in year two we started considering that maybe this thing wasn't going to bang out without some help. We weren't sure where the help should come from and struggled with the Ghostbustery question, "Who you gonna call?"

I kept starting to move forward, then having second thoughts and thinking we just needed to have sex more or have sex less or change up the timing or try leeches or shock treatments. Nobody knew about essential oils back then or I would've been allllll up in that. We would've had oils in all the orifices.

People choose different ways of pursuing help, and we tried them all.

#1: The wait and see approach

Just keep tracking your ovulation. Just keep having sex at the appropriate times. Lather, rinse, repeat.

#2: The extreme prayer approach

When things aren't taking their natural course, some of us decide to go above our pay grade, into the heavens. This can take many different forms, from lighting candles in church or [insert religious venue] to healing services where people lay their hands on your uterus and speak in tongues or smear oil on your forehead and speak a blessing over your womb.

Or maybe your extreme prayer isn't something you'd consider prayer. Maybe you start making deals with the universe, promise to call your mother every Sunday or stop stealing cable from your neighbor or vow to plant a tree, offset your carbon footprint, and do a better job of recycling. You might take meditation classes, learn how to align something like a chakra or an aura or light incense and write poetry in a meadow while wearing paper pants and a crown of flowers.

Whatever. You try to get pregnant through pleading, deal-making, or being a better person. This is slightly noble, but not necessarily effective, and if your prayers are not answered according to your timetable, it can leave you with a faith crisis, or just super pissy.

#3: The medical approach

When approaches #1 and #2 don't work, many people head for #3: Get Thee to a Doctor.

With the medical approach, you're going to encounter a couple of steps. First, let's diagnose the problem, and second, let's see if we can fix it. For many couples, either or both of these parts can take a while and involve exposing your goodies to many, many people.

We went with a combo approach, spending time praying and also getting my feet in some stirrups and testing Alex's junk to figure out the problem. You might work your way through a chain of doctors, from your primary care physician to your OBGYN to a reproductive endocrinologist, and eventually, you might pinpoint the source of your infertility and then work to solve the problem.

Or maybe you'll hear what I did, which is, "Yes, we've pinpointed the reason, your endometriosis, but no, we don't understand why that's keeping you from getting pregnant, because it's not like you have a clump of something clogging up a tube somewhere. It's more like you're a toxic environment for children." Okay, they didn't say that part, but I read between the lines.

While pursuing the Extreme Prayer Approach, I prayed that God would make the right path obvious and help me figure out what to do, and if God answered that prayer then I'm pretty sure God gave me fake appendicitis.

One night my lower right quadrant (that's what everyone at the hospital kept calling that squirrelly area around my right ovary) went berserk. The pain got worse and worse and we'd just had a visit from a friend who told us about his appendicitis. Fearing that my appendix would burst and poison my whole body, I went to the doctor, who gave me a rectal exam. There's nothing better in the world than a gloved finger up your patoot when you're wracked with pain. It's like, "Thanks, doc, feels all better now."

She sent me to the ER and they started running tests. They gave me

There's nothing better in the world than a gloved finger up your patoot when you're wracked with pain.

something fantastic for the pain, which helped me get over the anal probing I'd just experienced, and I had my first pelvic examination by a male doctor. It was a day

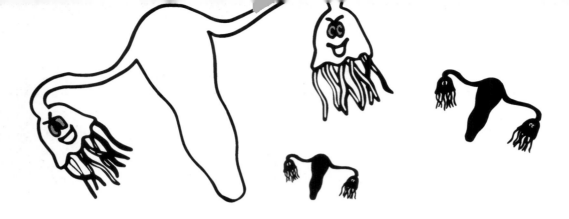

of firsts. They sent me home, without appendicitis or answers.

This kicked off a season of ultrasounds and tests, which ultimately lead me to a fertility clinic. The best thing about that place was I was no longer sitting in OBGYN waiting rooms surrounded by pregnant women. The worst thing was the overwhelming amount of information. Between the price tag and the decisions about embryos, it was a lot. The doctor told us to start with a laparoscopy to figure out the pain on my right side, a sperm count for Alex, and then we'd go from there.

During the laparoscopy, they confirmed that I had endometriosis and also got rid of as much of it as they could. They told me that some women were able to conceive after the surgery and to take a few months to try some more. The pain in my right side was still there, twinging away like my ovary was actually a jellyfish that stings me over and over all day long. But I hoped for the best, that I'd be one of the lucky ones who could get pregnant post-surgery.

I wasn't. Months crawled by, still no baby, and it was time to talk about intrauterine insemination (aka IUI, when they power wash sperm and squirt it inside you with a giant turkey baster...I told you this book was super sciency) and superovulation (when they use drugs to make you ovulate a bunch of eggs at one time, like an Easter egg hunt for your ovaries). We were officially starting fertility treatments.

If I were to create my own superhero, I'd call her SupHERovulation, and she'd have the power of Fertility. She'd swim the rivers and oceans on her chariot pulled by enslaved sperm men impregnating women with her fallopian tubes of power. All we'd have to do to call her is cry,

"SupHERovulation, help! My uterus needs you!"

Our first IUI failed after a weekend getaway to New York City. I had major allergic reactions to progesterone, so we met with the doctors and changed up a few things for round two.

Our second IUI failed at my brother's wedding reception between the salad course and the entrée. This did

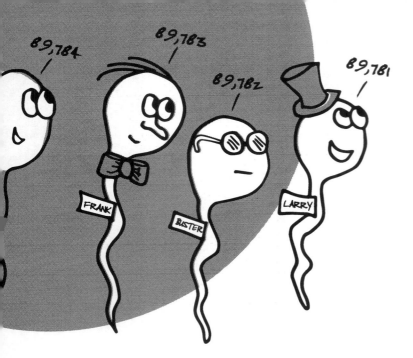

89,784

89,783

89,782

89,781

FRANK

BUSTER

LARRY

not feel like great timing. As the cramps overtook me, I excused myself to the bathroom and discovered the truth. No baby. I stood in the bathroom stall for a few minutes, took a deep breath, and returned to the table.

I leaned over and told my mom, "I got my period." I could see it in her eyes. She already knew. She has a sixth sense about her kids and those extra minutes in the bathroom tipped her off. She put her arm around me and ordered me a glass of wine. It's one of my favorite moments with her. There was this solidarity, where I felt like she immediately understood what I was going through, that I didn't want to

ruin my brother's wedding but I needed a moment. She'd miscarried a baby between me and my brother and she knew all too well the pain and loss. I was so grateful for her understanding. And the wine. I was way grateful for that. After it knocked the edge off the cramps – and the heartache – I got up and danced the night away in my green twirly gown with my husband.

It was still just us. It was awful, but we were together. I have photos of us dancing together and I look so happy. And yet I'd just experienced another death. Somehow that's how feelings work. We have grief and joy all wrapped up together in one moment on the dance floor, and I think the key to survival is making space for both of those emotions and letting them coexist as long as they need to.

Our third IUI never finished because I was in danger of ovulating too many eggs, getting pregnant with septuplets, and ending up on the news as a cautionary tale. (I always have been an overachiever.)

Our fourth and final IUI was almost as expensive as in vitro because they monitored me so closely after the last round. It didn't work.

We agreed to take a few months off and not talk about it. We went to the beach, and I watched Alex build a sand castle with some stranger's kid and resisted the urge to bury myself in the sand. I cried underneath my sunglasses. It was time to talk about in vitro.

I think Alex was hesitant to put that pressure on me, knowing that my body would bear the burden of all the procedures, so I told him I wanted to go for it. More about that later.

My biggest regret from the early years of our infertility is not being more proactive sooner. I kept waiting and trying to make sperm meet egg through sex and prayer. So by the time I sought help from a reproductive endocrinologist, I was already a strung-out basket case ready to drink snake venom or strangle a rabid puppy to get pregnant. I was tired and starting to fade away from the life I loved. I think if I'd gotten help sooner, I would've had more emotional stamina and stayed more present in my relationships.

I don't know exactly where you are in the process and what you're going through. I'm sorry for your losses, for your pain, and that this child you want so badly isn't coming when your heart feels so ready for it. If you're smack in the middle of trying to make decisions about procedures and specialists, hang in there, and I'm rooting for you.

ALEX

Just Be Cool, Man

I'm a wimp. At least that's what my wife tells me every time I complain about my annual prostate rectal exam. She just looks at me with that "oh, honey" expression and in that moment of silence we both agree I have no leg to stand on. But for the handful of guys reading this book ... solidarity.

Let's face it. My wife has it harder. Much harder. And my role is clear. I'm Super Supportive Guy. I attend appointments, hold hands, hold panties, whisper words of encouragement. But I don't always get it right.

The first time I took my wife to get a transvaginal ultrasound, I was so awkward.

I didn't know what to do with my hands, like I was giving a presentation without a podium. Do I put them in my pockets and try to keep this moment casual or do I fold my arms like a stern father watching a kid take his daughter on a date for the first time? I kept trying to make small talk with the doctor as he shoved the ultrasound wand up my wife. Melanie gave me her "shut up" eyes, but the words just wouldn't stop. *Where did you go to med school? How long have you worked here? Do you like your job?* It took all my willpower not to say, "How's the view?" I make jokes when I'm uncomfortable.

5 Tips for Seeking Help

01 **Research mode.** Get references, talk to other couples who went through it, and read as much as you can online. When you're at one doctor's office, get their recommendations for next steps. Get second opinions if you need to and don't be afraid to ask questions. Ask so many questions. Brainstorm questions ahead of time and have your list ready at your appointment.

02 **Talk with your partner** about options and how far you're willing to go. Lots of people are going to give you advice and once you start meeting with doctors they're going to have recommendations and want to start rolling. The most important relationship you have is with each other so have open conversations about what you're willing to do and how often. Do you have a cap on what you can spend? How are you going to finance procedures? You don't want to end up feeling pressured in an office and not being able to talk privately. You need to make sure one of you isn't thinking, "Let's try one medication," and the other is thinking, "I'm open to experimental human cloning splicing my DNA with unicorn chromosomes." (hashtag science)

03 **Be gentle with one another** because this is emotional and there's so much at stake and you're dealing with your physical bodies and future and the intensity of that can lead to a powder keg situation. I told myself no matter what happened, I wanted to come out on the other side of this with my marriage intact. We'd have each other, with or without kids.

04 **Spend some time considering which route** you want to pursue. Are you open to adoption or fertility treatments? Is trying to carry a baby yourself important to you or is surrogacy an option? Do you really want an infant or are you open to older child adoption? If you want to pursue fertility treatments, how comfortable are you with needles and doctors? What do you need to do mentally and physically to prepare for putting your body through these procedures? If you're open to adoption, how ready are you for the onslaught of paperwork and subsequent bonding and attachment process? (More about adoption later.) Visit with families who have gone through fertility treatments as well as families who have adopted.

05 **Let people know what you need.** Tell your partner, your doctor, your family, and your friends. Don't be afraid to ask for help. It's your body so you are your own best advocate.

Whether you decide to keep trying on your own, pursue adoption, or seek help through fertility treatments, the long road of infertility can do a number on your identity and you may find yourself questioning who you are. In the next chapter, we'll talk about struggling with your identity, watching the people around you get pregnant, and that freaking dreadful day, Mother's Day.

03.

IDENTITY

"Happy Mother's Day!"

Liz Lemon: "I want to roll my eyes right now, but the doctor says that if I keep doing it, my ocular muscles might spasm and eject my eyeballs."

-30 Rock

No. No. Not another invitation to a baby shower. *I can't do another one. I can't do the game where we wrap her belly in toilet paper one more time. I can't do a relay race with baby-dookied diapers. I can't do a baby food taste test. I'm not strong enough.*

Something about the entire event of a baby shower makes me feel like an outsider to the human race. Generations of women come together to usher their sister into a new dimension of womanhood. There are young girls looking forward to this future experience, older women sharing advice and stories of their own crowning achievements, and their literal crowning achievements, and countless peers in the prime birthing age in various stages of bearing, birthing, and nursing. There are enough hormones in the room to make me get my period just by walking across the threshold. And then there's me. This other woman, outside the circle of life.

There's a swirling fertile circle spinning life, and then there's this tender shoot off to the side, whose desiccated flower is crumbling. I'm not attached to anything. I don't make life. I'm just...me.

I hear the strains of "All by Myself" moping through the elevator music of my mind. *Snap out of it, Melanie. They'll have bacon-wrapped*

shrimp. All is not lost.

Somehow womanhood and motherhood have become tangled up into one big definition, but they are two different things. And there's a life stage progression that society thinks we need to adhere to, but it's not a rule, desire, or even a possibility for some of us.

The progression is this: first you're single, then you get married, then after the appropriate amount of time as DINKs (Double Income No Kids), you have kids, but just the right amount, not too many, not too few. Then you raise them, then transition to empty nesting, followed by retirement, followed by death. If you spend too much time in one of those categories before moving on to the next one, people start whispering, offer to set you up with their chiropractor's cousin's son who just finished law school, or slide pamphlets about sperm banks into your purse when your back is turned.

And there are these markers that remind us we aren't playing by the rules and need to get with the program. For some of us, it's Thanksgiving dinner when all the relatives gather to grill each other on our current job, dating, and womb statuses. For others, it's that plucky Valentine's Day, or Singles Awareness Day. For me, it's another holiday, the one in May.

Mother's Day killed my soul. It was this horrendous dance to celebrate the moms in my life while wanting to crawl in bed and never come out. The carnations at church might as well have been glossy cards with the words "#%@! you, barren girl" emblazoned across them.

"If you're a mother, would you stand?" This familiar scene played out in my church each year, and all the mothers would stand and everyone would clap for them. On the way out of the sanctuary, volunteers would hand the mothers flowers, and I'd have to shake my head no. *I'm not a mom. I don't qualify for your stupid flower.*

When I was in the middle of IUIs and getting nowhere, on Mother's Day I got in the car by myself, drove to the Krispy Kreme, and bought two donuts. One for each ovary, maybe. Never underestimate a well-timed donut.

"Motherhood is a woman's crowning achievement."

You push your shopping cart into the checkout line and subtly peruse the magazines that speculate on who's hooking up and what marriage is on the rocks and how to achieve the greatest orgasm you've ever had. And pregnant actresses. Pregnant singers. Pregnant seems to be the new look for spring. Everyone's rounded bellies are airbrushed and glowing. You look into your cart. Dinner for two. Just

two. The woman in front of you placing items on the conveyor belt has a toddler buckled into the cart and when she turns you see the outline of her pregnant shape. She unloads prenatal vitamins and organic mac and cheese and you feel the familiar lump form in the back of your throat. Motherhood surrounds you and you can't join the club.

You've suffered through twentysome years of monthly periods and underwire poking into your jumblies and now when it's finally time to activate your lady parts, they inform you they're just going through the motions and not really functional.

People breathe gooey sentiments about motherhood and mothers and yes, give those ladies all the credit they deserve, but what about you? If you're a woman without a child, where does that leave you in the hierarchy?

I definitely found myself questioning, *Am I even a woman? What am I?*

Society teaches us that motherhood is the greatest pursuit, and when we are unable to achieve it, we're left feeling like we've been denied our dream job, like we're on permanent disability and unable to work. We have to do a better job of celebrating the ways all women contribute to society, whether they're doctors or teachers or neighbors or awesome aunts. Mothers should absolutely be celebrated, and we need another day, too, for all women. Happy All Women's Day. You are amazing, regardless of the status of your cervix.

"You are cordially invited to attend one million baby showers."

I tried to stay tenderhearted toward the slew of pregnant friends and blue pee stick triumphs of others. I threw baby showers and made cute gifts and celebrated the people around me. But sometimes I had to give myself a break.

It's okay to skip stuff. If you're having an okay month and can make it to a friend's baby shower, fantastic, but if you've just received more bad news, call in sick. Stick the gift in the mail.

Fertles, if you're reading this, give a little grace to your friends who may need to flake out on your baby shower. Let them know you care and you're totally fine with them not being able to make it. Maybe later that week you two can grab a decaf latte together, away from the pressure of teacakes and pity glances.

You can skip baby showers, regular showers (I mean, occasionally, before you become a public health hazard), and all kinds of stuff. You can also skip the Mother's Day brunch. If you still want to celebrate your own mom or mother-in-law, see if she's cool with you bringing over mimosas for an in-home, low-key celebration without the chaos of an hour-long line at the local pancake house.

I am a mom now. I love moms and I love celebrating the crap out of ourselves come Mother's Day. But every year around this holiday, the old panic creeps up my legs into my sucky little ovaries and I look around wild-eyed at the waiting women, the hurting ones, my infertile sisters jacked up on hormone drugs praying fervent words of longing to a God they aren't sure is listening anymore.

Every year I'm for them. I'm for you.

I've never recovered from the inner cringe that happens every time Mother's Day rolls around. When Mother's Day is the worst day of the year...for so many years...it leaves a mark. Every day I think of you and ache with you, but this day in particular the wounds feel fresh.

If you've experienced infertility and now have children by birth or paperwork running around your house, you understand. This week we hug our kids a little tighter. They give us side eyes as we caress their sweaty heads and breathe sappy things into their ears. I'm thrilled, doing The Running Man happy dance, to get to experience motherhood and also devastated that my very name, Mom, brings pain to a woman who isn't in this place.

And so there's the tension. Of wild partying in the Mommy Club and intense grieving over the ones experiencing the pain that I remember too well. And I can't and won't resolve the tension, but instead acknowledge them both. I will woo-hoo *and* weep for the whole gamut of womankind.

On that baggage-laden Sunday in May, while recognizing the precious moms I adore, I intercede for the barren with prayers to a God I don't understand. I exchange knowing gazes and nod my head with respect. The wound is healed, but the scar is gargantuan.

There is more to you than infertility. Caring friends and family want to check in, offer ideas, and let you know they care, but it can feel like you're going from one pep talk to the next. It's exhausting and honestly kind of boring after a while, like there must be more to life than people with their heads cocked to the side asking about your ovulation and your husband's "healthy swimmers." Shut up with the swimming sperm talk before you ruin the Summer Olympics for me.

Unfortunately, each person you talk with doesn't understand that you've already had the same conversation seventeen times that week. They're like college professors who all act like their class is the only one you're taking so clearly you have one hundred percent of your time and energy to devote to Dante, Chaucer, and the socio-economic deconstruction of Beowulf. Only you know how tired you are. Only you understand how you're all out of *cans* and you are *can't-evening* so hard right now. You have to be the boss of the conversation sometimes.

What else you got? What else is going on besides babylessness? Did you read a blog post on how our phones are going to become self-aware and kill us? Did you get a new Ginsu knife that has revolutionized your life? Are you thinking about chopping off your hair or getting tickets to a game of sportsball? Steer the conversation to other, less traveled pastures. Divert divert squirrel!

For those closest to you, be honest. "I'm starting to feel like my uterine lining is a group project. Can we talk about something else? How's work going?"

Men going through infertility can also struggle with feeling secure in their manhood. Many men in our culture brag about their virility, their ability to get their wives pregnant on the first try like it's a symbol of their manliness and strength and not because a teeny tiny Michael Phelps swam into an egg and implanted in a fluffy uterine lining. (I know, more swimming. I'm the worst.) My husband Alex struggled with that.

ALEX

No Comb-Over Cure

Growing up I sometimes had trouble fitting in with other guys. I played sports, but I didn't care about watching it on TV, and I definitely didn't know it was the playoffs or the finals or even the Super Bowl. I was always like, "Is it that time of year again?" How did every boy in my class know the minutiae of professional sports? Was there a crash course I could take?

In middle school, I was often teased for my extreme lack of sports knowledge, getting a trick question like, "Who won the World Series, Oakland or the A's?" Or,

"What sport does Steve Yzerman play?" (Apparently, if you live in Detroit you should know this.) Let me save you the suspense, I didn't have an answer to either, but almost thirty years later, I still remember the questions. To this day, I still don't know what icing is – thankfully, now I live in a city that lost its hockey team.

I've been growing a beard. Something about a beard makes me feel more manly. It also covers a multitude of sins. Razor burn. Acne. Multiple chins. Although I have patchy holes in strange places.

That's how it felt when Melanie told me I should get my sperm count checked. Another hole in my manhood. Another reason to feel like I didn't measure up. But this one couldn't be solved with a quick comb-over. I agreed to get checked out.

When you're asked to pee in a cup, you feel a sense of accomplishment as you hand back a brimming cup of steaming urine. Not so much with semen. I remember staring down into the collection cup in disappointment. I failed. As far as I could tell, there wasn't enough for testing let alone impregnating my wife.

So many thoughts flooded my brain. In college, I had almost broken up with Melanie because she didn't want to have kids. It had taken years for her to flip that switch, and now I was going to wreck it. I felt sick to my stomach. Strangely, I wasn't afraid I would never have kids. I was afraid to shatter my wife's dream.

How to fix Mother's (and Father's) Day so it doesn't hurt so much

Acknowledge the pain. I didn't want moms not to get celebrated. Someday I hoped to join in. No, I wasn't bitter (mostly), but I just needed not to feel invisible on Mother's Day. I needed the leaders and friends around me to acknowledge the pain. I needed them to say something like this: "I know this day may be difficult for some of you. Maybe you're experiencing infertility, maybe you've felt the pain of miscarriage, or maybe your own relationship with your mother has been hard. Maybe you've recently lost your mother. We acknowledge this and recognize you today."

Let mothers (and fathers) identify themselves. Hey waiters at brunch, ushers at church, and everyone else in a position to greet possible parents on Mother's and Father's Day: let them identify themselves. Don't guess. Please don't guess. Even if someone looks about the right age for procreating and you see her body and think, "Those are great birthing hips." Do not. Assume. You know what they say when you assume. You make yourself a total buttmunch.

No one should shove flowers at women. Let us reach for one. And if you're a mother in your heart but not yet in your home, feel free to take the dang flower and hold it proudly. We got you. You're one of us.

It's okay to play hookie. It's also okay to skip brunch or church on Mother's and Father's Day. You will not lose your salvation if you take time off for self-preservation. This is totally okay.

5 Tips for Holding onto Your Identity

01 **Focus on who you are apart from your fertility.** You are not your womb. I became Melanie Broken Uterus Dale, but I had so much more to me than just that. Who are you? Who loves you? What are your gifts and talents and quirks, likes, and dislikes? Write them down in a journal, put Post-It notes around, or schedule daily reminders on your phone.

02 **Cultivate areas of interest** on your calendar, whether it's a weekly class or even just once a month. I joined a yoga class and while I was learning new poses, I looked at myself in the mirror and made myself appreciate how my body could move. It was letting me down as a baby-maker, but look how it could flow through sun salutations and find balance in tree pose. I would breathe in, practice gratitude for my body, and focus on the other ways it was healthy apart from fertility.

03 **Skip and serve.** This is a two-parter. First, like I mentioned, let yourself skip stuff if you need to. Some months are harder than others. Second, serve. Plug into your community and serve at a food bank or shelter, help your friends and family, or take a neighbor a meal. Serving others helps us feel needed and gets our minds off our own problems. Some months you might be in a hopeful phase and a baby shower is a fun opportunity to celebrate a friend and dream of when it's your turn. Some months that procedure you were banking on fails big time and you might not want to crawl out of bed. Skip and serve. You need them both. Find a balance.

04 Feed your creative side. Everyone has one, no matter what you do for a living. Go to a museum or gallery, attend a concert or play, or read books just for the pleasure of it. Immerse yourself in culture, form opinions, and let yourself respond to what you're seeing. Notice your response and value your own opinions and feelings.

05 Change something about your appearance. I know looks aren't everything, but I found that doing something fun with my look felt empowering. I got a tattoo, dyed my hair red, and bought a pink plastic belt that I wore constantly because it made me happy. Maybe for you it's a dress that makes you feel great or getting your nails done. Sometimes all I wanted to do was lie around in my sweats feeling bloated. Making the occasional change and wearing something that felt good helped me get off the couch.

In addition to attacking the very core of your identity, infertility can destroy your sex life. If your sex life is awesome and you're living the dream, you can skip the next chapter. But if you're like me, and infertility has made your lady parts dry up like the Sahara, I'll see you in the next chapter.

SEX

"At least it's fun trying."

"It's business time!"
–Flight of the Conchords

Hey baby, tonight's the night.

Sigh. Okay. Looking forward to it.

Yeah me too. Oh baby. Sexy time is the best.

I think the mere mention of sex made my eggs crawl back up my fallopian tubes and my husband's sperm self-immolate on the spot.

After about two years of trying to make a baby, our sex life consisted of charts and days and times and pee sticks and so much pressure that our sexy time felt like a graveyard of buried dreams. People would joke, "Well at least it's fun trying!" Oh absolutely. We are swinging from the chandeliers with wild abandon over here! We're not at all cowering with fear that our stuff doesn't work. No, this whole thing feels like a second honeymoon.

After about two months, it isn't fun trying anymore. And after two years, your vagina clamps up tighter than a hipster's jeans and your penis flops down and hides at the mere mention of ovulation. Your junk wasn't made for this kind of pressure.

"Are you doing it right?"

I actually had a coworker ask me this. A dude coworker. Um...I dunno. Maybe we needed a diagram or something. I tried standing on my head. I tried lying there to let the swimmers have plenty of time in the pool. (New game idea: every time I mention swimming you do a shot...of Clomid.) People made jokes about whether or not we knew what we were doing, and we secretly wondered if we did. You tweak up the timing, you try it a thousand different

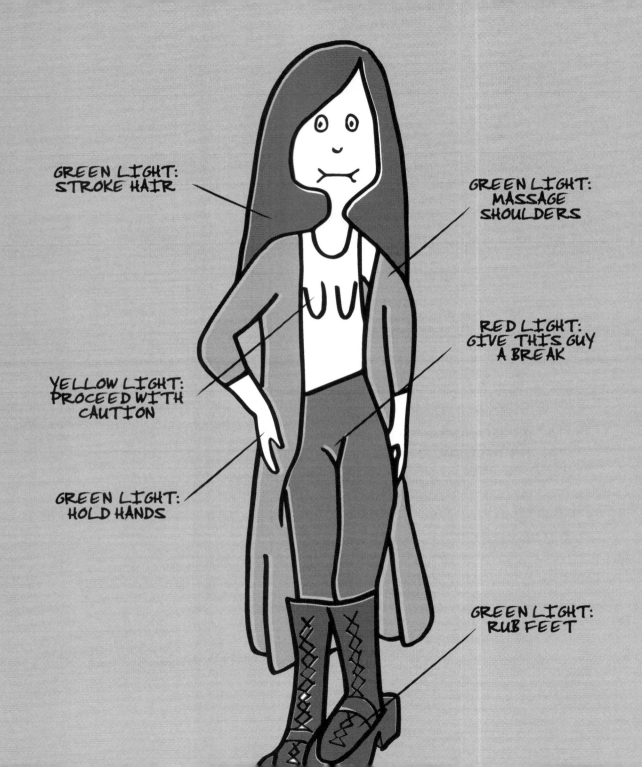

ways, and everyone has an opinion. Without alcohol. Before lunch. On a trampoline. What was supposed to be a fun romp between two people in love felt more like shooting a sex scene in a movie, with rote choreography and a ton of people in the room giving you direction.

I began to wonder if we really weren't doing it right. Maybe we couldn't get pregnant because I was really bad at sex. And the more you worry you're bad at sex, the more it becomes a self-fulfilling prophecy. Suddenly, you're up in your own head thinking through every move, analyzing the mechanics of it all, then your partner notices that you don't have your head in the game and asks, "Why do you look like you're going to cry?" You try to slide your face into an enticing smile, but it comes out more like a grimace and he asks, "Am I hurting you?"

Sexy time felt like a graveyard of buried dreams.

"No! I mean, yes, because my endometriosis glues all my organs together which makes sex painful, but for sure, keep going, I'm fine." He looks worried, and you finally put a pillow over your face so you can quit making awkward eye contact and just make an embryo already.

Drunk teenagers in the back of pick-up trucks can do this. Apparently people in airplane bathrooms can even do this. Why is this hard!?

"Let's talk about sex, [lack of] baby!"

So, sex can become incredibly not fun. It's such a mental thing and when you're thinking, *Just get the raw materials in the right place at the right time so we can make a baby*, it's not the stuff of Hollywood movies. Having sex while trying to get pregnant is like those new credit card chip readers in stores that beep at you. "Do not remove card...do not remove card...do not remove card...OH MY GOSH GET IT

FAILURE BED

OUT REMOVE CARD REMOVE IT NOW." It's a lot of putting stuff in the proper place then getting it out as soon as you possibly can.

Our sex life took a hit, so we worked on the rest of our marriage to stay connected. We went out for weekly date nights, hung out with other couples, and spent weekends binge-watching whole seasons of *Buffy the Vampire Slayer* while guzzling jumbo Slurpees.

Even years later, after the infertility, getting to the place where sex is enjoyable again has been a road. There's so much defeat and brokenness, and it felt like our bed was filled with failure.

After infertility, our sex life didn't magically snap into place. We were scarred. Infertility leaves its mark on your relationship and it takes time. For us, it took a lot of time. Something broke inside us. When your bed becomes the job from hell but you can't quit and you feel the weight of failure lying on top of the two of you, it's hard to recover.

I Hated Sex

I hated sex. I never thought those words would escape my brain – certainly not on paper for thousands of people to read. As guys, I think we try to maintain the appearance that sex is always fun. We ritually beat our chests like cavemen, but it's a façade. Sex isn't always fun. And after months of thermometers, ovulation calculators, and too much advice from pretty much everyone, I hated sex.

What's worse is that it stressed me out so much that I couldn't always perform when needed, which heaped piles of depression on my wife's head and guilt on mine. We were never going to have a child. It was all my fault.

Selfishly, when we learned Melanie had endometriosis, I felt a weird sense of peace. Disease was the culprit, not me, *not me*. It would still be years before sex became enjoyable again.

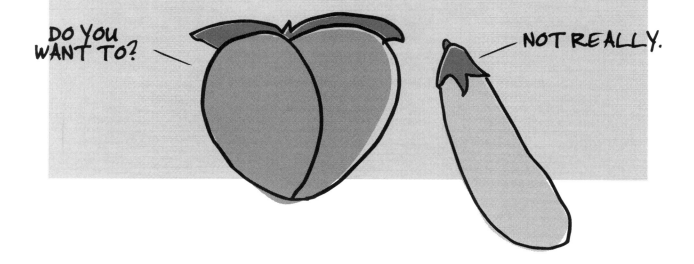

5 Tips for Sex

If you're struggling to perform or enjoy sex during or post-infertility, you're not alone. It was a long road for us. Here are some things that helped:

01 **Spend time together** and declare at the beginning of the night that you're not having sex. It's a sexless hangout time. That way neither one of you is sitting there tense and worried that at some point on this couch watching *Batman Returns*, you'll have to strip and go to town. Take the pressure off at the beginning and then enjoy just sitting next to each other. Sometimes you have to rediscover that your bodies are safe places, that you can be with this person without pressure to perform with this person. Communicating out loud that tonight you're just going to enjoy cuddling means you can breathe and laugh and not worry about an erection calling you to duty at a moment's notice.

02 **Be there for each other.** If one of you needs attention and the other one is still in a fragile place, the off-duty person can be there for the active duty person. The important thing is togetherness, so stay together, help each other, but don't demand that both of you have the same physical and emotional needs at exactly the same time. You've lived with pressure for long enough. Take that pressure off.

03 **Focus on the small things** like when you first started dating. My OBGYN actually gave me this idea when I shared with her how difficult it was. She told me to focus on the feel of his hands. So we started holding hands, and I thought about his hands. When you first started dating, when you first touched fingers and held hands, it was electric. After you've been in stirrups with a turkey baster up your veejay in front of him, it's easy to forget about the little things. So start from the beginning, before ovaries and stirrups and sperm counts. Start with hands and go from there. I'll leave it at that.

04 **Do stuff that's never gotten anybody pregnant ever.** The thing that's helped us rediscover our love for sex and get us over the debilitating failure is doing things that can't get you pregnant. I mean, not just me because I'm infertile, but things that have never gotten anyone pregnant in the history of the whole world. Don't make me draw you a diagram. Just find new things to do and enjoy them without any pressure or thought of babies being made. Just because you can, pressure free. Take pregnancy out of the equation. Find other things to do.

05 **Look at your calendar** and plan for those weeks when you're ovulating. Keep your nights pretty open, schedule a massage, or take a walk. Like with any job, prepare for success. Whereas before infertility maybe your pants hit the floor and you were raring to go the second you got home from work, maybe during infertility you need more preparation to get interested in sex. Spend more time making out first. Make dinner or have take-out delivered with multiple courses, and for each course take off an article of clothing.

Hey, I was thinking. After talking about sex, what could make this book even more awkward? Ooh, I know, let's talk about religion. Ever feel judged about fertility treatments by a religious relative, or has your own faith factored into your decisions? The next chapter is for you.

os.

FAITH

"Just wait on the Lord."

Patty Tolan: "That's where I saw that weird sparking thing."
Jillian Holtzmann: "What was it?"
Patty Tolan: "Baby, if I knew what it was, I wouldn't have called
it a 'weird sparking thing.'"
—*Ghostbusters*

My face burst into flames as the person I thought was a friend stood on stage at a church speaking about the evils of in vitro. She'd never said anything to me, and now she was using her platform to speak out against a procedure I'd been pursuing for a whole year.

I looked down at my belly, swollen near the end of my second trimester. With my in vitro baby. My miracle. The boy who lived, after so many failed attempts. I felt my insides go steely, this newfound mama bear sharpening claws ready to protect my boy from anyone who thought he shouldn't exist.

I practiced my Lamaze breathing, also an excellent anger management tool. *Back off, church lady.*

If you're part of a faith community that has various opinions about making babies, then you know the added pressure when you add God's people into the mix. My husband and I are both Christians, and since our fellow Christ-followers had quite a bit to say about our infertility, I'd be remiss if I didn't include it here. If you come from a religious background or maybe have a religious aunt or grandma who

NOOOOOO!

weighs in on your choices, some of this may resonate with you, too. If God isn't really a part of your life, you can either skip this chapter or read it as an interesting anthropological study.

We found ourselves smacked with the question, "How far is too far?" Just because scientists can do it, should we let them? Our faith community collided with medical procedures and we had to navigate the sticky world of embryonic ethics. If the theologians and politicians couldn't agree on what was right, what hope did a couple of desperate wannabe parents have? This one is so interesting to me, because we never tell Grandpa not to get the kidney transplant and just wait on God. We don't tell kids with leukemia to skip treatment and wait on God. We like to pick and choose our science. I experienced judgment for doing in vitro and freezing embryos and people publicly spoke out against my decision.

This chapter isn't about telling you what's okay and what's not, but it's about helping you shut out the noise, seek God, and decide for yourselves. I believe that at the intersection of science, personal experience, and faith, you'll find clarity on where you're comfortable and where you want to head.

At the time, I felt like the only Christian woman on the planet going through infertility, certainly the only Christian undergoing fertility treatments. Weren't Christians supposed to pray harder and make deals with God, not turn to doctors and scientists?

Looking around church, seeing hordes of children running between legs, nurseries

packed to the rafters, and sermons on parenting containing jokes about making babies, I decided that I must be alone.

I attended church groups and celebrated with couple after couple as they announced good news. Everyone offered prayers, but no one had answers.

When I've written about infertility on my blog, Unexpected.org, and in my last book, *It's Not Fair*, I've had women privately message me with their struggles. In the Church, baby

dedications and sermons on getting married and having kids abound, while infertile couples suffer in silence.

Throughout our battle with infertility, I read books, threw books, prayed, fasted, went to church, avoided church, and contemplated suicide. I desperately sought out advice and a faith-based perspective on infertility and received an ungodly amount of judgment and advice to relax and wait. I needed someone with whom to talk about everything from how God feels about embryos in a freezer to the sexual

dysfunction created by the pressure-cooker of our baby-making bed.

"Just trust God."

When I mentioned to church people that we were struggling with getting pregnant, they often assumed I was a big fat God-doubter and they'd remind me to keep trusting the Lord. Many people had variations on this one, like somehow my faith was crumbling and I needed a good spiritual enema to stay on the God-train. It was a little offensive. I was Trusty McTrusterson, and what would they know about the inside of my heart? I wasn't struggling with my faith. I was just hurting. I didn't understand and I wanted God to fix it, but my God was still good. I didn't want to switch Jesus out and try a different god or anything.

If the people in your life are reminding you a little too often to keep trusting God, feel free to give it right back to them. "You too! Keep trusting God with your school tuition and shin splints and voting! Trust God at the buffet at Golden Corral! Never stop!"

"God's timing is perfect."

Maybe the religious version of "You just need to relax" is "God's timing is perfect." To which I gasp, "You mean God doesn't want me to have a baby right now?!?" How dare someone say that to you.

Lots of people told me to wait on God. Yes, we should absolutely wait on God, follow God, not get ahead of God. But. Would someone tell a cancer patient not to go seek treatment? How did people decide when to wait on God and when to move forward and follow the people God created and gifted to help? Who made the rules and decided what constituted waiting?

God has blessed us with medical interventions. We slowly, prayerfully took it step by step, waiting on divine direction, but not just sitting around for a baby to go POOF! in my belly. God's timing can include going to the doctor. People do it every day.

"That's unbiblical."

Why couldn't there be a book in the Bible called First Reproductions, nestled between Galatians and Ephesians, which laid out the exact way to handle infertility the God-way? The Bible has a lot of stories about how people took infertility into their own hands. There are stories of God "closing" and "opening" wombs, men impregnating their servants when they couldn't knock up their wives, one of a dude getting smote for "spilling his seed" on the ground instead

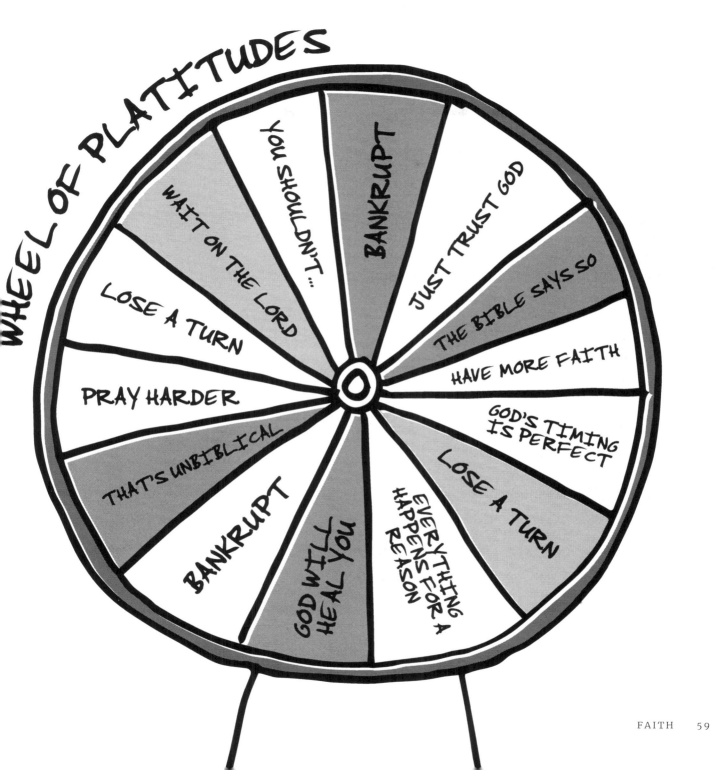

of in his wife (I'm looking at you, Onan.[2]), but nothing about reproductive technology. But in all fairness, the Bible also neglects to mention airplanes and antibiotics, so...could just be that it hadn't been invented yet...is all I'm saying.

We made the excruciating decision to cancel our third round of IUI because we would've had to sign something that we were not comfortable with, that we would allow "selective reduction" in the event I ended up with too many embryos. I didn't want to reduce anything. We weren't personally comfortable with selective reduction because we thought if we were trying so hard to make the embryos we wanted to give each of them the opportunity to grow into a whole person. But these choices are hard and nuanced so we're not going to judge someone else for making that choice.

I've heard people condemn surrogacy and donor embryos because they're bringing other people into a marriage relationship. As we've built our family through in vitro and adoptions, I just think there are lots of ways to create family, so let's all support each other as we're trying to make our own decisions.

Everyone stop judging people. Babies are babies, no matter how they're created.

The lovely ones

Religious people can be judgy people, and I can say that because I'm one of them. We like to think our opinion on something, church history or our interpretation of scripture, is the only way to do things. We need to resist this inclination in ourselves and protect ourselves from other people's judgment.

Obviously, there are a lot of judgy people in our faith communities, and it's an unfortunate reality. But I'd be remiss if I didn't also talk about all the lovely ones. I'm so thankful for the supportive relationships we had during our struggle with infertility.

Our church group fasted together for a day before we started in vitro. They gave up food and spent the day praying for us when those

---

[2] Genesis 38

hunger pangs reminded them, and then we gathered for BLTs at our friends' house at the end and they all prayed in person with us. It was the sweetest, most loving moment of community. My mother-in-law stayed with us and helped out when I went in for a procedure. One of my parent's friends sent a ginormous box of books for me to read

There are lots of ways to create family, so let's all support each other as we're trying to make our own decisions.

through when we were in the decision-making stage. Some I liked and some I threw across the room, and I was so grateful for her thoughtfulness.

After my embryo transfer, when I was on bedrest and feeling nervous and urpy, the women in our church group came over to watch movies and hang out. They listened while I read one of my journal entries and they just sat with me. There are wonderfully supportive people out there who offer

community and comfort. I think if Jesus was still walking around, he'd be one of them.

How the bloody unclean woman taught me to chase after my healing

I love the woman in the story that Luke, who was a doctor, records in chapter 8 of his account of the life of Jesus. Jesus had been asked by Jairus, a synagogue leader, to come heal his daughter, and on the way to his house, Jesus had to worm his way through a crushing crowd. A woman in the crowd came up behind him. She'd been dealing with bleeding for twelve years. I don't know the specifics but I wonder if she had endometriosis or ovarian cysts. I picture that she had her period for twelve years straight with no tampons and no hope of healing. And in that culture, that made her ceremonially "unclean." Under Mosaic Law, she couldn't go to the temple, offer a sacrifice for her sins, or engage in community. For twelve years she was considered an unholy social pariah.

And one day she heard about Jesus and that he was there. Everyone else heard, too, so there was a U2 concert-sized crowd pushing around him. But she was willing to throw aside her pride, propriety, and cultural norms of the time to do anything for healing. She wound her unclean self through the crowd to get to Jesus, and knew that if she could just touch the edge of his cloak, she'd find healing. She knew he was the answer and she just had to get to him. When she touched the edge of his cloak, her bleeding stopped immediately. She was healed.

Jesus felt the power go out from him and asked who touched him. In a crowd of people pressing all around him, he felt something different. This bold woman, unclean and cast out for twelve whole years, was shaking and terrified but in front of the crowd she fell down at Jesus's feet and told him why she'd touched him and that she'd been healed, and his response kills me. He tells her that her faith healed her. He exhorts her to go in peace. And then he goes on to Jairus's house and raises the dead.

Anyway, that bloody woman demonstrated faith by seeking out Jesus in that crowd. Plenty of people would say we should just wait on God and trust God for healing. But that woman didn't wait. She didn't wait, see? She took her unclean self and got in that crowd and pushed through that crowd and cast aside all propriety to fling herself at healing. She did whatever she could do to get her healing. She didn't wait

for Jesus to come to her. She didn't hope that he'd come by. She went after him. She gave it all she had.

Fertility treatments were me trying to touch the edge of Jesus' cloak.

I don't know what's right for you, what gels with your beliefs and your faith community, but be like that bloody unclean woman. Chase after your healing.

How Gideon reminded me that statistics aren't everything

(Spoiler alert: in this next section I'm going to talk about in vitro a bit, and also I get pregnant the one time. Skip it if you don't want to hear about that right now.)

Our first attempt at in vitro failed, and the wait to reboot my body and try again felt interminable. Halfway through August, hopped up on copious amounts of mood altering drugs, I decided to start a journal filled with all the things for which I was thankful. It was burnt orange, my favorite color, and I scribbled down my gratitude for "flip flops, carpet that doesn't show dirt, Calder's mobiles, non-shedding Yorkies...swashbuckling butt-kicking fantasy adventure stories of super-heroicism, weird words...ceiling fans...punk...my neti snot pot...weird humor, well-developed characters with lots of quirks." Looking back over my long list, I see that apparently I was very thankful for my neti pot and anything weird, because I wrote about them several times.

At the end of August, the doctors took out my eggs and combined them with Alex's sperm, and every day we'd get a call with an update about our offspring in the little tube. It's strange. What happened in that tube is similar to what happens in uteruses all over the world, but we got to hear about every step. What we wanted was a "Day Five Blastocyst." (I was a THEATRE major so if you don't know what a blastocyst is, you are not alone.) Those are the strongest embryos and our chances of a pregnancy would be fifty percent with one of those. (Also, remember how I said at the beginning that the science has probably changed since I went through everything? For all I know "Day Twenty-Seven Blastocysts" are the bomb diggity now or they actually grow the whole baby outside of your uterus in little pods like in *The Matrix*.)

Each day they'd give us the update. We started with

twenty eggs from my egg retrieval, fifteen of them getting jiggy with sperm. Wow. Okay, yes, since we had committed that any embryos we made we'd come back for, even if it took us a decade, we were like WOW! We're going to have a giNORmous family! One of the women who shared her wisdom and experience with me had told me they ended up with seven healthy embryos. *Seventh Heaven* here we come!

But then each day, the report would come in, and there would be fewer and fewer thriving embryos. This happens in the body naturally and most women never know they have tiny two-day-old pregnancies that don't thrive. Hearing about it with a blow-by-blow every day was weird.

Fewer.

Fewer.

Fewer.

Nevertheless, on day five, I woke up excited for the call to tell me READY! Come in and get test tube LAID! The call came. None of our remaining little guys were ready. In that moment, our statistics dropped to a thirty percent chance. Lying in bed with Alex that night, I started praying out loud. I sobbed to the Lord, wretched, exhausted woman. Alex held me, didn't say a word, and just let me cover my pillow in tears.

And when I was done, God spoke back.

Not audibly, but I felt God rumbling in my spirit so clearly. *My child, when did this become about numbers? This is about me.* I opened up my Bible to Judges chapter 7. Gideon. The story of Gideon's army. I'm not a military person, but infertility felt like a battle so this account resonated with me.

'The LORD said to Gideon, "You have too many men. I cannot deliver Midian into their hands, or Israel would boast against me, 'My own strength has saved me.'" Gideon started with 32,000 men going into battle against the Mideonites. He was unbeatable and could totally take all the credit when he trounced them. But again and again, God whittled down his army, fewer, fewer, fewer, until he was left with three hundred measly soldiers. And then God won that battle for Israel. At the end of the battle, there was no question how they did it. God did it for them.

In my thankfulness journal, I wrote the following entry on September 5, 2006:

Judges 7. Today God reminded me in a big way that he's in control. Not just saying it, thinking it. Knowing it. Humbled by it. I thought in vitro was in his hands. I thought I trusted him. I did. But when my safety net of frozen embryos and plenty of healthy ones just waiting to be babies was ripped out from under me, I got scared. And I realized that I shouldn't have a net. I didn't know I did until it was gone. I still had 32,000+ battle-ready soldiers with weapons to fight my Mideonites, and today God reminded me that I just need him. Three hundred exhausted soldiers wielding torches and trumpets. And the God of the universe calling the shots. Truly, "an army of One." I'm glad my safety net got yanked. Rip it to shreds; throw it away. Tomorrow I go into battle with God. My enemies don't stand a chance.

"Not by might
Not by power
But by my Spirit, says the Lord."[3]

The next day, day six, the lesser of the embryo days, we got the call. Better late than never, future kids. Our chances were lower, but I remembered Gideon and that it's not always about numbers. I'm grateful for a Day Six Blastocyst transfer. It was a divine reminder that I didn't trust in statistics. I trusted in God.

And after the transfer of two little embryos, as I lay there still NOT being allowed to pee after they pushed an ultrasound into my extremely full bladder, we signed a form and halfway down the page, it said that we had two embryos to freeze. A surprise. We didn't think we had any.

In my thankfulness journal, after "chocolate brownies, good coffee," but before "being by myself so I can fart," I entered this: "9/18: I'M PREGNANT ahhhhh!!!!!" God had defeated my Mideonites.

At this point if hearing that someone got pregnant AND that she thinks God had anything to do with it is making you Hulk out, please feel free to rip this book in half with your bare hands. Or scoff at me. I can take a good scoffing. Do what you need to do, and I'm so sorry if my story hurt you. I've tried to reflect honestly about my journey with science and faith, but my story is just that, mine, and yours might look totally different. I thank God for my pregnancy, but God didn't love me more when I got pregnant, nor did God love me less when all the other attempts failed. God loves us all the time, during all the procedures, even when it really doesn't feel like it.

---

[3] Zechariah 4:6

Frozen

Sometimes my brain goes to strange places. The first time I heard about embryo cryopreservation, my mind flashed to Han Solo frozen in carbonite in Jabba's Palace. Then it pinballed to Austin Powers, Khan, and even Phillip J. Fry in *Futurama*, who thaws out 1000 years later with a sexy alien girlfriend and a robot buddy, ready to take on exciting new adventures. Could that be our embryo's future?! I snapped back to reality and tried to focus on what the doctor just said.

"Fifteen of Melanie's eggs have been fertilized."

Fifteen!! Like fifteen kids? My mind was swimming.

When you realize you've fathered a small village, a twinge of nervousness settles in. Before you can stop yourself, you're breaking out the mental abacus to figure out college tuition.

Before we started the IVF process, Melanie and I made the choice to continue until we'd implanted every last embryo. These were our kids after all, and we weren't comfortable discarding them or even giving them up to an embryo adoption program. But there I was thumbing through the cryopreservation brochure, frozen – unsure what this meant for our future.

As the week progressed fewer and fewer embryos remained viable. Fifteen quickly became ten. Then eight. Six. Five. It wasn't looking good. I wish I could say I prayed extensively about this, but I didn't. Part of me was ashamed. At first there were too many embryos, and now there might not be any. How could I ask for help when I couldn't seem to trust God with the results?

The familiar lump of disappointment stirred in my throat. Thankfully, after several days, two little blastocysts made the cut, while two prepared for their cryo-nap. Sometimes, even when you can't face God, he has a way of reminding you he's still there anyway.

5 Tips for Navigating Faith

01 **Seek wise counsel.** People talk a lot about getting "wise counsel," and this is important, but decide what your criteria for "wise" is. Not every jerk with some holy scriptures and an opinion is wise. Choose your counselors carefully.

The most important people who need to be in agreement are you and your partner. That's it. Everyone else may have opinions, and you can decide who you want to listen to, but at the end of the day, the only ones who matter are the two of you. Be firm with others and choose ahead of time what you're going to share. You might need to do all your research ahead of time before ever presenting the outside world with your decision.

02 **Seek people who have gone before you.** A pastor's wife I knew introduced me to a family in her church who had kids through in vitro, and while I watched this mother nurse twins at the same time, she talked about her experiences with getting pregnant and how she and her husband made

decisions about leftover embryos. I was so grateful that she invited this total stranger into her home to ask completely invasive questions and I always try to pay it forward with people in my community who are struggling with infertility. Do you have any regrets? How did you come to the decision? How did you deal with friends and family who were judgmental? How much do you tell others or keep private? How did you budget for fertility treatments? What do you wish you'd known at the beginning? What are you doing with the other embryos you have waiting in cryo?

03 **Seek God.** Spend a ton of time on your knees and in your Bible. Get close, even if you're mad at God for this whole thing. Ask all the questions you think won't ever get answered. If you don't know what to say, read Psalms out loud.

Be honest with God. If you don't like "Your will be done," say so. I think the most important thing with faith is staying connected, and sometimes in a relationship when things aren't going well, we need to be honest and share our deep feelings, even if they're not pretty. If you are struggling with trust, spell it out: "I don't trust you, God. Help me trust you. Help me want to trust you." That's a step. Relationships are messy, even divine relationships, and it's okay to be messy.

04 Seek doctors. When it comes to finding your comfort level with your faith and fertility treatments, research is your friend. The more you can read, pray, and ask questions of both doctors and clergypeople, the more peace you'll have about whatever decision is right for you.

First, consider the science. Google everything you can and make a long list of questions to ask. What does the procedure entail? What happens to your body? What happens to the eggs and sperm? What happens to the embryos? What are the statistics? At first I was freaked out about in vitro but the more I asked questions and read and educated myself about the materials in the test tube and how what's happening in the test tube mimics what happens in a fertile woman's body, the more I came to terms with statistics and accepted that regular women lose embryos frequently and never know they're pregnant. The process of some embryos making it and some not progressing happens in wombs unbeknownst to would-be parents all the time. So I no longer saw the test tube as a tiny murder chamber but as an incubator for life. We had a front row seat to every single cell division and I realized that God is in that test tube just as sure as God is knitting a fetus together in a womb. Sure, we can put sperm and egg together just like Fertles do when they copulate, but only God can make them into an embryo. Only God can make it viable. Only God can make it grow into life.

You might develop a completely different understanding and might be led to all different kinds of things. Get as many answers from doctors and science as you can so you can make an informed decision. What's right for you is that middle part of the Venn diagram where science and your faith live in harmony.

05 Seek gratitude. Like I mentioned, I kept a thankfulness journal throughout our in vitro process that helped me stay positive and focused on what God had given me and not just what God hadn't.

It helped swat the bitterness away on days I
was feeling less than thrilled about the hand
I was dealt.

We've talked about the judgy religious people and the lovely religious people, so now let's
talk about all the other supportive people and what to do when they "just want to help." Bless their
hearts.

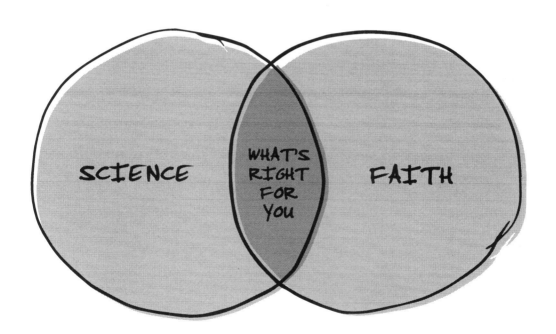

06.

OTHER PEOPLE

"Have you tried...?"

Westley: "I'll explain and I'll use small words so that you'll be sure to understand, you warthog faced buffoon."

–*The Princess Bride*

Don't you love it when people try to encourage you? "My cousin couldn't get pregnant for ten years, lost thirty-two babies, tried to kill herself, but then finally got pregnant, so maybe you'll be that lucky, too!" Thanks, that's reassuring.

People want to help, and so they give you advice. "Have you tried adding ____to your diet/____position/____time of the month/ measuring____/doing a fertility dance?" All useful suggestions. Thank you. How do you handle the well-meaning advice-givers without driving yourself crazy?

Honestly, in their defense, I set an impossible standard. I wanted people to check in and provide the perfect amount of empathy, compassion, and support, and I also wanted everyone to stop asking how things were going. I wanted someone to rub my back and make pity noises while also not touching me and leaving me alone to sit in a dark room by myself. I wanted people to come over and I also hid when the doorbell rang. I wanted someone to help me find a solution but got really mad when people talked about it and gave me ideas.

If you're reading this as a friend or family

member trying to be supportive, I have no easy answers for you. Your person might want to talk about it every day for five hours straight or maybe she wants to punch you in the face. My advice is to let her guide you. Just show up ready to be with her, and let her decide if she wants to talk about it or not. Sometimes we just need to go to the movies or grab coffee and throw stuff off a bridge.

And if you're reading this and you were my friend when I was battling infertility, you were of course perfect and I'm clearly not talking about you.

Types of Fertles

There are several different kinds of Fertles staggering around like Walkers on *The Walking Dead*. At any point you may stumble upon a herd of them and it's helpful to understand them so you'll know how best to take them out.

Types of Fertles

Empathetic Fertle

She got pregnant on her honeymoon and likes to joke that all it takes for her husband to knock her up is for him just to breathe on her. Motherhood is her reason for living and she wants so badly for you to experience it, too. She'll start to tell you about her kids, then tear up when she thinks about your childlessness, then tell you more about her kids. She hopes that some of her fertility will rub off on you simply by proximity. She offers for you to babysit her six kids whenever you want so you can practice parenting.

Exhausted Fertle

Motherhood is the worst thing that ever happened to her. She spends hours telling you how hard it is and how you're so lucky not to have to deal with nine hours of soccer tournaments on a Saturday and being up all night covered in vomit. She regrets everything and tells you often how she wishes she could switch places with you. She'd give anything to have just one day in your shoes, barren and childless. She thinks it sounds like a permanent vacation.

Egotistical Fertle

She wants you to get pregnant yesterday so she'll have a mom friend. You want to give her the benefit of the doubt that this isn't her only motivation, but you're simply basing this conclusion on every word out of her mouth. No one understands what she goes through, and if you had a baby, too, then you'd truly achieve her plane of existence and could bond at a deeper level. These silly friends without kids can never understand what it's like to carry life and then wipe life's butt.

When Fertles try to encourage you

"You have plenty of time."

People told me a lot that I was so young, that I had plenty of time to get pregnant. While that's true, I was young with plenty of time, if it wasn't working in my mid-twenties, I had a hard time believing that a decade would increase my chances.

I'm so young. Yes, yes, that's true. Shouldn't getting pregnant be easier then? I mean, my eggs were youthful and vivacious and ready to grow into a person, right? When we finally had our first appointment with the reproductive endocrinologist, she said that because I was so young, I shouldn't be having these kinds of problems. Thank you! Yes, exactly!

When you start using the i-word, people try to reassure you that everything is fine, which makes you doubt yourself. Maybe you're worrying too much. You waffle back and forth about whether to keep waiting or maybe talk to some people about next steps.

I wish I hadn't waited so long to start figuring out what was wrong. For two years, we just kept diligently trying, I kept peeing on a wide array of plastic sticks, popping vitamins, and staying healthy. Around the two-year mark, I started wondering if I should go get things checked out, or just keep waiting and hoping. It took me two years to admit we had a problem, because we kept hearing how we had plenty of time to sort this out. Don't listen to people who minimize your concerns.

"You just need to take your mind off of it."

I read somewhere that infertile women are second only to cancer patients in what they are willing to undergo to achieve a cure for their disease. I believe this. I would do anything. My career in costume design was beginning to grow and I was surrounded by people I loved, but nothing else mattered except the next shot, the next treatment. Insurance papers and phone calls crept in, my folders of paperwork grew, and I became less and less able to handle life, relationships, and work. I didn't care about anything except my desperate need to be a mother. I was supposed to be a mother, but I felt trapped in gridlock, and every

day was *Groundhog Day* with no hope of moving forward. I would have vivid dreams about being pregnant, and the next morning I'd wake up with the feeling still enveloping me. When I opened my eyes and realized it was all a dream, I'd feel crushed under the weight of my unmet need.

So when people told me to take my mind off of it I found it literally impossible to comply. Fertles who haven't been through it don't understand all that goes into treating infertility, just like I can't understand what it's like to have cancer or diabetes. It's maybe like being on permanent disability and you can't go to your job that you love. You want to do the work of being a mother, but your body won't allow you to. You're stuck on the sidelines watching other people go to work.

If well-meaning friends are encouraging you just to take your mind off your treatment, encourage them to bring you a latte and a fuzzy blanket. *Shh, friend, less talky more helpy.*

"Is it okay if these forty-seven other people observe you?"

I had one procedure done at a teaching hospital, with students in and out of my vagina, I mean operating room. It was awkward and weird. If you've ever had something done at a teaching hospital, you've probably had the

pleasure of an entire classroom's worth of young doctors-in-training clomping through your room. I'm grateful, really. I had a laparoscopy performed by the doctor I chose. The only catch was I was equivalent to the mealworms I observed on my desk for second grade science class.

Beyond feeling like a mealworm in a petri dish taped to a young scientist's desk, when you're experiencing infertility, you can feel like everyone in the tri-state area is aware of your ovulation, sperm count, and whether or not you were able to perform sexually. You feel exposed for everyone to see. All I can tell you is remember that the medical staff ogling your lady garden is so used to it that they don't remember your garden at all. For some reason, they've chosen to ogle gardens for a living, and we're glad they have, but yours is in no way memorable, no matter what your college boyfriend told you. Unless you decide to shave their name into your junk hair or dye it purple, they will leave that room and never remember you. Keep a low profile, mealworm.

"Have you tried...?"

Now what about the advice-givers? I still get twitchy when people start sentences with "Have you tried..." and the invention of Facebook sometimes makes me want to burn down the internet. I'm so glad we weren't advising our friends online yet when I was going through everything, and I'm so, so sorry for the world you're living in. Everyone has a new diet or product they want you to try that will fix all your problems. And many people really do care and want to help.

Let me empower you that it's okay to look someone in the eye and say kindly, "Don't try to fix this." You can't spend hours receiving more input. It's too much and you already have enough on your plate. You can take control of when and where the input happens. For your own sanity, you need to. Have your partner serve as a bouncer at your nightclub and toss people out if you need to.

ALEX

Broken Record

When I was young, I remember listening to records in my parent's basement. I can still smell the musty jacket covers. My favorite album was Don McLean's "American Pie." When you're a kid, there's something impressive about memorizing eight minutes of folk rock. But toward the end of the song, there was a scratch that made part of the chorus repeat until we kicked the record player – "This will be the day that I die, this will be the day that I die, this will be the day that I die..." Definitely a chilling place for the record to get stuck.

As a guy, it's sometimes hard to let other people into your life. You've got this. You don't need help. And when you struggle with something for years that feeling is magnified – you get tired of sharing the same hurts, complaining about the same issues. You're a broken record, and you're stuck on a really sucky refrain that casts a dark cloud over everything. Before long you can almost hear your friends clear their throats when you walk into the room, or see them shift their weight in their chairs when you open your mouth. Everyone nods politely and provides comfort ... after all, they're your friends. But you can tell the mood has shifted.

So for the sake of your relationships and your pride, you shut down slightly. You put on fake smiles and limit your responses to "I'm fine." The battle rages on inside you, but you do your best to manage the spillover.

Unlike my wife, I welcomed talking about our infertility issues with our more superficial friends and acquaintances. Let's refer to these people as Friends Lite or Diet Friends. I wasn't paying for therapy (although I probably should have), so besides my wife, these were people I could talk to. They hadn't heard my song and dance a million times, so my record wasn't broken to them. I could unload a little without feeling like a burden. I'm not saying this is a healthy practice, but I did find a degree of solace in it during the later years of infertility. I was just glad to talk to someone.

5 Tips for Dealing with Other People

01 **With friends, be honest** with them when you don't want to talk about it, when you just want to go out for margaritas and chips and not think about the thing that's hurting you so much.

02 **Let your partner play executive assistant** – all inquiries go through him. When I was taking all the shots and my ovaries were the size of grapefruit and I was a homicidal rage machine, I could not handle a whole lot of superfluous family members up in my business all the time.

They called Alex, and he decided what, if anything, I needed to hear. He deflected the questions and kept everyone at bay and let me choose when I wanted to deal with people. "I'm sorry, she's in a meeting right now. Can I take a message?"

03 **Learn to advocate for what you need.** Practice saying, "I don't want to talk about that," "That's personal," or if you want to avoid confrontation but not divulge information, "We're fine; thanks for asking." Don't hang out with people who don't respect your boundaries.

04 **If you're trucking along with some fellow infertile friends** and one of you gets pregnant, woo-hoo the crap out of that and also allow some space for the tension between celebration and anguish. It's okay to feel multiple feelings. It's a time for rejoicing and letting yourself grieve that you all can't be pregnant. Come together for support but don't feel like you have to share everything. Establish this freedom ahead of time, before anyone gets pregnant, so that no one gets her feelings hurt.

05 **Keep a list of stupid things people say** to you and read through it and laugh with your partner. Bless their freaking hearts. Fertles can be so obtuse.

In addition to dealing with well-meaning friends, if you go the medical route with fertility treatments, you also will become a pro at coping with various procedures, from medicines and blood work to insurance agents. In the next chapter, we'll talk about some things that help.

07.

COPING

"You might feel some mild discomfort."

Nursing Home Orderly: "Good news, everybody,
we're extending arts and crafts time by four hours today."
–*Happy Gilmore*

The walls zoomed away from me as the floor buckled under my feet. The light narrowed to a pinpoint in my eyes as my stomach contents leapt up my throat. I was alone, naked except for the thin hospital gown gaping open in all the wrong places. I clawed at the hospital bed parked in the hallway, grasping for anything to break my fall.

A nurse found me and helped me to the bathroom, reminding me helpfully that the procedure I just had shouldn't have caused the pain I was feeling. I threw up in the sink. Guess my body was weird and I was a lightweight snowflake with a low tolerance for pain. Add it to the list of ways I was failing as a regular human being.

After my hysterosalpingogram, I learned to become an advocate for myself because I knew my body better than anyone. I asked the advice of friends who were doctors and nurses and they empowered me to speak up. When people would come at me with needles I'd say assertively, "I need a butterfly needle because my veins roll and I need your best phlebotomist. I'm extremely dehydrated, drink entirely too much coffee, and have been already stuck in the same spot seven times this week. My veins are blown out and I need to know that you can tap this vein on the first try." Nicely. I said it nicely, because I didn't want them to poke me harder. I learned to apply pressure and raise my arm in the air after a blood draw, use ice packs to numb the muscle before an intramuscular injection, and sing '80s songs at the top of my lungs to keep my sanity.

"Your body is going to go through some changes."

The monthly letdowns take their toll, and if you add fertility treatments on top of everything, both your brain and your body will be a hot mess. The drugs will make you feel like you're in menopause one month, then pregnant the next, and continually going through a cycle of grief and loss while on estrogen and progesterone will mangle your brain.

Invest in comfy clothes that make you feel good. It was a hot D.C. summer where the humidity envelops you like the inside of a wet shower cap and I was blackened and bruised and felt like my insides were swelling to the point of bursting open my pale skin, stretched over blue

and purple veins popping out like Bane from Batman. I was rehearsing the play I'd written for the inaugural Fringe Festival in an old warehouse theatre with no air conditioning and I often thought about just floating away from my body. I bought a sundress from Old Navy. It was billowy and plaid, and I gained at least fifty pounds when I put it on, but the purples and reds made me happy and matched my veins and it was so lovely not to have fabric touching my middle, where I'd been injecting myself every night.

I had a lot of bruising and scar tissue in the muffin top region. Tight waistbands were my nemesis. I bought a soft nightgown that made my swollen boobs look amazing, so I felt comfortable and when I caught sight of myself in a mirror I didn't want to barf. And I bought a lightweight robe with flowy sleeves that felt romantic and pretty. Some of the drugs I was on gave me hot flashes and night sweats, so lightweight was key.

I had track marks up and down my arms like some kind of junkie, except I think my drugs were more expensive and they didn't take me away from my problems.

"Your embryo transfer has a fifty percent chance. Unless we have to do it tomorrow. Then your chances plummet to thirty percent overnight, but don't forget to stay calm."

Statistics will take over your life and you'll feel like you're living a word problem in math class. Find a way to manage your hopes without letting the statistics trample your hope. Stats are important because they help guide us to what procedures have the greatest chance of success. We need them to help us make decisions. But if we let our hopes get wrapped up in stats, they will disappoint us. No one should ever hang her hopes on anything math-related. I certainly learned that in Algebra II. So figure out where you can place your hope, besides numbers. For some of us that's faith. (I talked more about this in Chapter 5.) When I felt like the numbers were overwhelming me I'd realign my brain by praying and acknowledging that God's the boss of numbers.

For you, maybe it's not God. Maybe it's something else. Hope in more than numbers. Whether you're praying or lighting a candle or laughing with a friend or kissing your partner, focus on the truth and beauty in your life. No matter what happens, cling to hope that you will have goodness in your life.

"What is wrong with you?"

Oh so much. Sometimes you might go through depression. I numbed myself with

THIS VILL NOT HURT, AHAHAHAHA

television. Hours and hours of meaningless reruns while I sat in the dark. I was depressed and didn't realize it. Neither did my husband, who wondered if I was just super lazy all of a sudden. People came to the door and I hid. I ignored the ringing of the doorbell. When service people had to come inside to repair something, I felt so ashamed, lying on the couch while they worked hard fixing my sink or refrigerator. I shut myself into rooms away from the eyes of other people. I felt displeasing to everyone in the world.

Sometimes you might have bad reactions to procedures or medicines. After my egg retrieval, I scarfed down a Panera panini in the car on the way home, but immediately threw it up in the paper bag from whence it came. Anesthesia and hunger don't always play nicely, so take it easy and nibble slowly.

You might feel like a vampire's personal plaything. Despite watching every episode of *Buffy the Vampire Slayer* multiple times, I don't actually know what it's like to have a vampire suck my blood, but I think years of fertility treatments must be the modern-day version of what Bram Stoker's Lucy Wenstra went through with Count Dracula. They poked me so many times they ran out of places. I wish the vampire could've put me under his thrall so I wouldn't notice how much it hurt, and because my veins are stupid, they often had to have several different people attempt to get the blood they needed. It was like a phlebotomist's version of Pin the Tail on the Donkey: Tap the Vein on the Barren Chick.

And there's homework. So much homework. I had weekly and sometimes daily phone calls with insurance companies and billing departments that felt like a part-time job keeping track of all the payments and procedure codes.

So depression, vomit, vein implosions, and paperwork. I was a really fun person. If you're going through any of this, big hug. Well, I would hug you but I know it might hurt your arms.

"Fill this cup."

I mean, if I'm being perfectly honest, I get a little snarky about the challenge of what my husband had to go through on our quest for a baby. I mean, I was a human lab rat, with bruises up and down both arms and everyone all up in my vagazzle. And what did Alex have to do? Give himself a happy and try to hit the cup. I would've gladly switched roles.

There's this room called The Collection Room (ew) down a hallway in any fertility clinic. I think I speak for everyone when I say we all wish we could disappear into an abyss and secretly enter this room without anyone seeing us, talking to us, making eye contact with us, or in any way acknowledging our existence. Because only one thing happens in this room.

YOUR PENIS IS DWAYNE 'THE ROCK' JOHNSON

NOBODY LIKES A SHOWOFF. CALM DOWN, PENIS.

PAT YOUR PENIS ON THE BACK. JOB WELL DONE.

RESPECTABLE PENIS. NOTHING TO BE ASHAMED OF.

BUCK UP, LI'L PENIS. YOU HAVE OTHER QUALITIES.

Being the supportive wife that I am, I didn't want Alex to experience this by himself; after all, he'd been faithfully holding my undies in ultrasound rooms and I figured I owed him the same courtesy.

When we walked in the first time, we immediately noticed that the room had been set up for success, with stacks of inspiring magazines featuring scantily-clad women passionately dedicated to helping us get pregnant. In one room, there was even a naked mountain climber. I felt bad for this woman, suspended on the side of a slope with nothing to protect her nether region except the ropes between her thighs.

Alex and I decided ahead of time that we'd like to keep porn out of our baby making experience, even if our experience was already a little different than a bottle of Chianti and a John Mayer CD. "Your Body Is a Wonderland" takes on a whole new meaning when you're in stirrups and the doctor is explaining that your freakish ovaries make too many follicles and you're in danger of septuplets.

I flipped the magazines facedown and hung my purse over the poor girl on the cliff. We locked the door, and I provided the inspiration instead. Look, it's awkward and abnormal to treat a doctor's office like we were joining the Mile High Club but at least we were together.

The best thing about the worst thing that ever happened to us was that we were together. Through my painful procedures and his...hey, not fair. At least we were together. I was already feeling less-than as a woman and struggling with my body, and if Alex had turned to another woman, even an air-brushed one on a page in a magazine, to do his part of the procedure, I would've felt even worse.

ALEX

The M-Word

Masturbation. Yikes, it's tough to even type that word. In college, we had a number of creative euphemisms for this as you can imagine — playing Uno, walking the dog, pulling rank, polishing the rocket; no one wanted to say the M-word. I think my favorite was visiting the golden arches, which of course, made me never want to eat McDonalds again. Ok, who am I kidding? Now I'm thinking about Dollar Menu Double Cheeseburgers. But I digress.

Fast forward to infertility land. The M-word is still awkward but now there are brochures and videos and female nurses giving you directions. Part of me wants to joke that I am well-practiced and need no advice; the other part of me wants to slink into the corner and die. Can we not talk about this? And enough with the direct eye contact. Please just avert your eyes, hand me the cup, and say nothing.

I walk back to the "collection room" – like giving it a clinical name is somehow supposed to sanitize the purpose of the room and make us forget that there were 100 other guys in here right before you. Yeah I'm not sitting in that chair.

On the wall, there's a woman rock climbing a snowy mountain peak. She's not wearing pants. The poster is there to "help" me, but all I can think about is how cold she must be.

I fumble the collection cup in my hand. Next to my name on the label is a long set of digits. There are definitely a lot of infertile couples.

I'm about to "get started" when I hear the happy birthday song outside my door … I mean RIGHT OUTSIDE MY DOOR. Are they singing to me? I instantly zip up – afraid the door is somehow going to magically fly open and the clinic staff is going to greet me with a cake. I crack the door. Great. They're celebrating a staffer's birthday right across the hall. I think the whole office is stuffed into my part of the hallway. I catch a few glances as I peer out. One tech gives me the "are-you-done" nod. I shut the door.

5 Tips for Coping with Fertility Treatments

The drugs, stomach shots, butt shots, and emotional and physical drain of a pharmaceutical kaleidoscope running through my body took its toll. Let's talk about what I did to help with all the blood work, needles, waiting rooms, and shots at home.

01 **How to deal with blood draws:** You know your body better than anyone. Speak up and tell people what you need. Drink lots of water on blood draw days. Stay hydrated. Play music that distracts and uplifts you.

My mother-in-law had a friend who was a reproductive endocrinologist, and she gave me some advice about blood work. I was getting really bruised from multiple pokings a day, and she said after they take the needle out and put the cotton ball on the hole to stop the blood, don't bend your arm. Picture a puncture wound in a straw. If you bend it, it opens the hole and makes it worse. So she said to push the cotton ball on the hole, straighten my arm, and hold my arm up in the air to make the blood flow the other way. It helped.

If you feel faint, don't be a hero. Tell them.

02 **How to deal with injections:** Ice the injection site until your skin feels numb before injecting yourself. Don't you worry – you'll still *totally* feel it once that needle breaks the surface, but the outer numbness will give you the strength to break on through to the other side.

Sing '80s tunes at the top of your lungs while doing it.

03 **How to deal with insurance:** My mother taught me how to deal with paperwork. She's the most organized person I know, and she told me early on to start a file. I had a big hanging file for my filing cabinet, and within that file I had a whole bunch of folders. Insurance, reproductive endocrinologist, OBGYN, ultrasound place, lab work. Keep all your receipts in there and plenty of blank paper for taking notes. Whenever you talk to anyone on the phone, ask to whom you're speaking and write down her name, extension, the date, the time, and everything she says. That way, when you're on the phone with the insurance company for instance, you can pull out all your notes along with their paperwork and say, "Now when I spoke to so-and-so on the phone on March 1, she said this." It's like going down the rabbit hole, and the more clues you leave yourself the better chance you have to make it back out alive and with some of your stuff paid for.

04 **How to prepare for appointments:** Keep a notebook and write down your questions for each visit. Leave space for their answers, and write in the answers as you receive them. Staple or tape in receipts or keep them in your folders (See number three).

As for preparing for his appointments, if, like me, you aren't really into other people's naked pictures but can't get away to the collection room with your partner because of your work schedule or the overwhelming awkwardness, consider sending him a few private photos on his phone to inspire him.

05 **How to deal with bad news:** One of the hardest parts of coping with infertility was obviously the month grief cycle. I'd let my hopes get up, and I'd feel good while I was injecting myself with something and getting ultrasounds. As long as I was feeling proactive, I was okay. But then the big moment would come, I'd get a blood test, it would come back negative, and I'd experience a death. Again and again. Each month my dreams turned to ash and blew away.

To cope with this deadly cycle, I began having a night out. Because I was trying to turn my body into a temple to fertility and take the perfect combination of vitamins and water and positive energy, I was eating pristinely and not touching alcohol or caffeine. So on those weeks when I'd find out I wasn't pregnant, Alex and I would go out for dinner, I'd drink a margarita, run to Starbucks for coffee, or do whatever I'd been craving that month.

During particularly difficult months, after getting bad news, I'd give myself a whole day to lie in bed reading fiction books or watching *Legally Blonde*. "The bend and snap...works every time!"

Before we went for our final in vitro, we told ourselves that if it didn't work, we'd go to a spa together. It gave us something small to look forward to even if all our hopes and dreams were dashed into tiny pieces. Hey, I am all about finding the bright side. Sure enough, after we got the bad news, we headed to the spa and started the long road to healing.

Most importantly, let yourself mourn. You are experiencing a monthly death, and it takes a huge toll on your spirit. Give yourself the grace to grieve. You need freedom and space to let your heart, and your body, heal after yet another traumatic experience. Call a therapist if you need to. I did.

Okay, that's how to cope with bad news, but what about when you get good news? I mean, that's what we're hoping for, right? I need to spend a chapter on pregnancy. I know sometimes it's hard to even read about, so if you want to skip it for now, please feel free. I'm including it because I do have some things to share about pregnancy after infertility, but you can feel free to throw the book across the room and scream all the words. Your call.

PREG-NANCY

"Once you get pregnant you're completely fine."

Peter Quill: "I don't need to hear how my parents..."
Drax: "Why? My father would tell the story of impregnating my mother every winter solstice."
Peter Quill: "That's disgusting."
Drax: "It was beautiful. You earthers have hang-ups."
–*Guardians of the Galaxy Vol. 2*

(If you don't want to hear about pregnancy at all, just skip this chapter. Feel free to sharpie this whole section like a redacted CIA file. I get it. Sometimes pregnant people gave me hope and sometimes they gave me rage.) My son is eleven now and knows how babies are made. The cool thing about in vitro is that when he was little I could explain to him that because Mommy and Daddy love each other, one day we went to the nice scientists in the lab and they took some of Daddy and some of Mommy and put it together in a test tube and made Elliott. It's as good an explanation as the stork and actually true.

"You want a Day Five Blastocyst."

Fertility treatments have more statistics than baseball. I'm actually not sure if that's true. I don't know baseball, but I do know infertility, and there are a whole lot of statistics. Every procedure you do has percentages of success, and you decide whether or not something is worth $10,000 for a fifty percent success rate, a thirty percent success rate...or worse.

We started our first attempt at IVF in the spring of 2006. We went all the way up to egg retrieval, only to hear that my follicles and eggs weren't doing their thing properly. Cancelled cycle. It felt like hitting a chute in the game Chutes and Ladders and we were back at the beginning and Lord Licorice was laughing at us.

I had to wait for a full natural cycle to swing through, which meant pleading with my uterus daily to start my period. *Come on, endometrial lining. Slough already. Nobody likes a lazy sloughing uterus.* When my cycle finally cycled itself in the summer, we hopped back on that horse...or more accurately, back on the needle.

COUCH
POTATO
UTERUS

Just Stick It in Me

"Just stick it in me!" my wife exclaimed. If it had been a decade later, I'd be uttering Steve Carell's legendary catchphrase from *The Office*. We were racing to finish progesterone injections during commercials between *Alias*. This was before everyone had DVRs, so we were constrained to watching television in real-time like utter cavemen. We take our girl-power, ninja kicking shows seriously, and I was letting down the team with my sluggish technique.

The first time I gave Melanie a shot, I carefully surveyed her butt cheeks for the right spot for like 20 minutes. At the fertility clinic, they give you a pamphlet and a prosthetic butt to practice. In my head, I knew there were no vital organs in her butt, but have you seen the size of that needle?!? I half expected it to poke out the other side.

Thankfully, it didn't take long to turn hormone injections into a game. I drew two eyes and a smiley face across her backside with a Sharpie. We'd ice her down during our favorite shows, and then I'd alternate between eyes for each shot. We'd gotten so good at it I probably could have played darts with her butt ... probably.

"The test came back positive."

We started in vitro again and this time we made it all the way through egg retrieval and embryo transfer. For two weeks, we waited with bated breath and I tried to stay perfectly still. I hate exercise so this was not hard.

I went in for my blood test that would determine our fate, and later that day when the nurse called I thought my heart would pop right through my chest. She was so deadpan and monotonously said, "The test came back positive." The test came back positive. Positive. I replied, "Okay. Does...does positive mean...am I pregnant?"

"Yes. Yes, you're pregnant."

"OH MY GOSH I'M PREGNANT? I'M PREGNANT!"

Nurses of the world, don't be afraid to woo-hoo a little.

Alex and I wooed and we hooed...and then the terror kicked in.

"You need to calm down."

The hardest thing about getting pregnant after infertility is how the pressure tries to steal your joy. You finally did it. You finally got pregnant after all that time and effort, and now you're afraid to breathe.

After my embryo transfer my mother-in-law came to help me while I was on bedrest. She installed a baby monitor next to my bed in case I needed anything and one night when it was really quiet she spoke through the monitor to ask if I needed anything. I jumped out of my skin and then started sobbing, thinking the fragile little embryos had probably just gone shooting out my vagina. I could not calm down and because my mother-in-law is Wonder Woman who can convince anyone to help anyone, she tracked down my doctor on the phone late at night and got me calm enough to talk. My doctor assured me that the embryos were like putting a piece of sand in peanut butter and spreading it on shag carpeting and rolling it up. One startle wasn't going to shake them loose.

I was relieved, but this kicked off about twelve weeks of neurotic behavior until one day I was crying so hard I felt my uterus contract and I realized I had to stop reading books about pregnancy and figure out how to enjoy this. I was trying so hard to have the perfect pregnancy that it was destroying me.

I had the guy at Subway microwave my lunchmeat to kill listeria (this is a solid idea) and tried to avoid driving near any other traffic so I didn't inhale fumes. In Northern Virginia. Where every single road is jam-packed with vehicles at all hours of the day. My mom said she felt sorry for our generation, because we know too much. Back in the seventies you just got pregnant and wondered if it'd be a boy or girl, but these days, we know every moment, every growth stage, and every toxin endangering our spawn. We work ourselves into stressballs trying to cross every t and dot every i.

After the first trimester I decided to back off and just try to enjoy this thing I'd thought about nonstop for years. I was so excited to have a baby belly that I started wearing maternity clothes at the first hint of an expanded waistline and I walked around the baby stores fondling all the crib blankets and staring at the breast pumps in dewy-eyed wonder. My second

It's in My Hair

"It's in my hair," I muttered to the guy next to me. The Lamaze class teacher had smeared peanut butter over doll butts in a mock poo explosion to test our diaper skills as hopeful parents. The brown pasty muck was all over my shirt and somehow had gotten in my hair, too.

Melanie was home on mandatory bed rest, so I was flying solo. The guy next to me was also sans wife tonight. We had turned diaper changing into a game of who could finish the quickest. Regardless of who won, I'd definitely lost at this point.

All around us couples were tag teaming with baby wipes. In the spirit of realism, each doll had a different mess to manage. I was cleaning up what could only be described as a Number Three. And it was everywhere. Thankfully, the room smelled like Reese's Peanut Butter cups and baby powder. It was a nice delusion considering what was waiting us parents down the road.

trimester was exciting and fun. And then my third trimester got a little too exciting.

"Once we get you pregnant you're completely normal."

I asked several different people on the team trying to knock me up if I would have a "high risk" pregnancy. I always received the same answer. "Nope! Once we get you pregnant you're the same as everyone else." And then seven months into my pregnancy, everything went wonky and I began seeing a whole list of doctors. And these new specialists in my life were saying, "In vitro? Oh yes, those are high-risk pregnancies. We just attended a conference on this. The rates of intrauterine growth restriction (IUGR), preeclampsia, and gestational diabetes are much higher with in vitro pregnancies." I had two of the three, IUGR and preeclampsia.

I'm sure you will not. I'm sure my story is like watching a reality show on Lifetime and nothing at all akin to your actual reality. Do not fear. My life is here purely for your

Your lady parts perform adequately. Every check up is routine.

An agreeable yet determined midwife strokes your perineum while you dilate and the baby crowns.

You give birth in a backyard koi pond. In the middle of rhythmic breathing, baby just falls right out.

REASONABLE
AMOUNT OF
RISK

LOWER
RISK

LOWEST
RISK

DEFCON
ONE

HIGH
RISK

Call in the specialists
that insurance charges
double for but it's worth
it when you don't die
and stuff.

Not only will this baby
likely Kill you, you worry
it might Kill everyone,
a la Rosemary's Baby
or that hybrid from
Twilight. You're going
to need some holy water
and a priest and the
Winchester brothers
from Supernatural.

entertainment. You will be fine. Here's what happened.

Around week thirty-two at a routine check-up my midwife discovered that I was measuring small and sent me to the hospital. I waltzed in there confidently, declaring to anyone who would listen that my husband was a small baby, I was a small baby, and so of course our baby would be small, too. Everybody please stand down.

Before I knew it I was stuck on bedrest collecting my urine in plastic jugs, counting kicks to make sure my baby was still alive, and going to the hospital for testing every few days. They kept admitting me then sending me home, admitting me then sending me home. My kidneys weren't doing so great and apparently my pee had a lot of protein in it. I pictured little hotdog chunks floating around. Nobody wants hotdogs in their pee.

The perinatologist told me my placenta looked like it was 110 years old. He kept monitoring it every few days and it was all dead looking, and yet, plain as day, we could see the blood pumping through it delivering nutrients to my little guy. Somehow the days crept by. I found myself wanting them to just take him out because an incubator in the NICU had to be safer than my body. The doctors were hoping we'd make it to thirty-seven weeks so he could get a little bigger. We made it to thirty-four.

I'll never forget that April 15 when my blood pressure flew way into the stratosphere. They had told me to get to the hospital when it reached a certain place so that I didn't stroke out and die. And here we were, on a Sunday, spiking into the danger zone. But I had an appointment already first thing the next morning and no baby of mine was going to be born on tax day, TAX DAY of all days. He'd end up being an accountant or what if we forgot his birthday because we were too busy working on our deductions? I hated math too much to let this be his life.

As long as I lay on my side all day, my blood pressure stayed low enough. The second I raised my head from the pillow, highway to the danger zone. So I lay there all day without moving, hooked up to the blood pressure monitor, counting kicks to make sure he was still alive.

The next morning, I showed up for my appointment and didn't leave until that baby came out.

I don't usually get scared about medical stuff, but I've never felt like such a failure, an alone, terrified failure, than when they shoved that needle in my spine before my c-section. After months of planning for a natural birth, I was prepped for a squat bar and some deep breathing techniques but ended up with my arms strapped out to the side and a sheet between me and my gaping insides.

As they pulled the placenta out of me, I heard them gasp, "Look at all the clotting! It's partially abrupted. It's a good thing we got him out."

They whisked him up to the NICU and I didn't see him for twenty-four hours. They started pumping me full of magnesium to keep me from having a stroke. I think I know how Johnny in the Fantastic Four feels, because I could definitely shout, "Flame on!" I spent the night puking up ice chips and trying to cool my fiery skin, my eyes swimming and my brain totally loopy. I kept feeling like my baby was still in there. He was inside my belly. He felt like a phantom limb that you still feel after it's been severed. My mom and Alex gave me updates. Elliott was doing great. I was not.

My sutures wouldn't stop bleeding and my blood wouldn't clot. I remember going cold and shaking uncontrollably as the doctor and Alex peered over my stitches while they sprang a little blood fountain. The doctor mused, "Hmm. I've never seen that before." I started freaking out about the freezer babies who still needed me and in my haze I worried I'd lose my uterus and strand my babies in the freezer.

(Hey, just poking my head in here to remind you that I'm sure this won't happen to you. Nothing like the mental picture of a blood fountain to freak a girl out. Don't even worry about it. But, you know, keep reading and stuff, because you made it through the blood and guts.)

It all worked out. Elliott spent ten days in the hospital and I spent six. I always say that my first selfless act as his mom was ditching my birth plan to do whatever it took to bring him into the world. And we both made it.

I'm not telling you any of this to frighten you. You will have a perfect, Beyoncé-level pregnancy, of course. I just wish going into my pregnancy that I had entertained the idea that I might not be Beyoncé. So while of course, of COURSE your pregnancy will be perfect, maybe prepare for a broad range of scenarios. Prepare to throw out the plan and do what it takes, because you know how many people I talk with about my birth story these days? Zero. Exactly zero. There comes a point in your kid's life when who he is supersedes the way he came into the world and he's Elliott the Brilliant Reader and Fantastic Swimmer rather than Elliott the Test Tube Preemie.

"You kept your babies in a freezer?"

I tell my son I saw him first swish into my body. Most people don't talk about the moment of conception with their kids. Ew. Aren't we all relieved.

But I remember watching on the ultrasound monitor when the turkey baster delivered him into my womb. It was a swish. A little puff. A swirl of life bursting into my fluffy endometrial lining. I watched it happen. As I was signing acknowledgment of our embryo transfer that led to our son Elliott, I noticed on the sheet of paper that they'd frozen two embryos. We'd talked at the beginning and come to an agreement as a couple about our commitment to any embryos we created, so we were prepared for whatever happened, but we were completely surprised to find out that we had two babies in the freezer. I began praying for our freezer babies right then.

After Elliott turned one, we started preparing to go back for our freezer babes. Since we'd moved to Atlanta, I did what they called "bus stop monitoring," where I went to a local clinic down here for all my blood work and ultrasound monitoring, then flew up to D.C. for the actual embryo retrieval. I know a lot of people take their embryos with them when they move, but I envisioned us trying that and getting stranded on the side of the road when our car breaks down in the middle of nowhere and me screaming, "We only have SEVEN MORE HOURS for these embryos to be viable," and us

living some kind of sick buddy comedy about an infertile couple who will go to any length to get their babies to safety against all odds. It would be the sequel to *Rat Race*, with Kathy Bates and her squirrels and everyone's racing to a big freezer rather than a cash prize. Along the way we'd make friends with a truck driver who'd let us ride in the back, but the cryo tank containing our spawn would fall out when the truck hit a bump and go rolling down the freeway with us scrambling out trying to catch it.

This was an actual thing that could happen.

I flew up for a "mock" embryo transfer, like a Renaissance festival for your uterus, but the jousting is with ultrasound wands. They play pretend, map everything, and do a full trial run on the procedure, then you go home and wait some more.

Back in Atlanta, I did all the drugs like last time and felt like a pro. This was not my first rodeo and I knew just what to do. But my body didn't get the memo and didn't seem to react as well to the drugs. I knew I had progesterone issues. Over the course of the IUIs and the last in vitro, we'd discovered that I had allergic reactions to taking it orally and vaginally, but the subcutaneous horse needle injections had never failed me. Alex shot me up every night for an entire trimester and I was fine. But this round, my body developed scar tissue faster and I had red lines of allergic reactions spidering out from the injection sites on both sides of my back. Every injection felt worse. What was going on?

I soldiered through, and the next time I flew up to D.C., my parents kept Elliott and we grabbed a hotel room right by the clinic. They thawed out my li'l guys and gave me the good news. Both embryos survived the freezer and were alive and kicking and ready to implant. C'mon, babies, get in my belly. Badabing, badaboom, I spent a day eating room service in bed, then we flew home.

Over the next few weeks I felt super preggers and started to tell family that I thought it worked. I pulled out my maternity clothes and figured any second my belly would pop back out like after turkey on Thanksgiving.

But it didn't.

The call that I wasn't pregnant knocked the wind right out of me, because it was so dang unexpected. I really thought I was. But I don't regret letting myself hope, because if you've been going through infertility for any amount of time, you know that hope is hard to cling to but sometimes you have to give yourself over to it in order to survive. I needed those two weeks of joy, even though they made the reality more crushing. Worth it, and I'd do it again. I'd hope again and again. If you're afraid to let yourself hope, I say do it. Manage your expectations, but let yourself delight in a little hope against the darkness of despair.

If you're afraid to let yourself hope, I say do it. Manage your expectations, but let yourself delight in a little hope against the darkness of despair.

5 Tips for Pregnancy

01 **If I had it to do over**, I would've read more about high-risk pregnancies and c-sections. I treated it like a taboo subject and wouldn't even read those chapters in all the books. Hope for the best, but plan for the worst, so you aren't caught off guard. Make the birth plan of your dreams, but be ready to throw it out at a moment's notice.

02 **That being said, enjoy this time.** Let yourself enjoy it. No matter what happens and all the things you have to plan for and think of, let yourself laugh uncontrollably and burst into tears in the diaper aisle of the store. Let yourself be happy. Good grief, you've earned it. Sometimes we just need to wallow in hope. Wallow. Let the hope get all over you. Even when I did that during my next in vitro, the one that failed, I didn't regret the moments I spent feeling happy and dreaming of the future. Those dreams weren't wasted and eventually turned into something else.

03 **If you've felt a little on display** during the complicated conception of your baby, now is your chance to dial it back and regain some privacy. Those relatives and the church prayer chain might be a-knockin' at your cell phone for all the details, but you can determine who gets top secret clearance to hear about the thickness of your cervix and whether or not you tore up your yam during delivery.

04 **If you're doing in vitro,** decide with your partner ahead of time exactly what you're doing with any and all embryos created. How many will you implant at one time? Will you freeze any leftovers? What happens if you break up, get a divorce, or one of you dies? Yes, this is awkward so I'm bringing it up for you now so you can have that awkward conversation. Are you both okay with another couple adopting your embryos through a program like Snowflake Embryo Adoption? Are you okay with extra embryos being used for stem cell research? Are you okay with them throwing out your embryos? Figure all this out before you're on a table with a full bladder and they thrust a clipboard at you.

05 **Practice open-handed parenting.** Release your baby. I don't mean out into the wild. It's not a tiger cub. I mean, every day, take your balled-up fists and open them palms up, breathe out, and say, "I release my child." (I say this to God, that I'm trusting God with my baby, but you can release your baby to whomever you want, the universe, Gaea, or Daenerys, Mother of Dragons. It's your baby.)

Once I had Elliott, I would feel the panic rise up at the thought of something happening to him. I think all parents go through this, but it's harder for those of us who have spent so long and gone through so much to have our babies. Literally opening my hand and exhaling out my control issues helps me relax and enjoy parenting, and probably makes me a more enjoyable parent.

With my increasing allergic reactions, I knew deep down that I wouldn't be able to handle another round of in vitro. Even if I could physically manage it, my body was rejecting the drugs and I certainly wasn't a paragon of health for an embryo to nestle into. We'd had one successful in vitro. It was time to throw in the towel. My days of fertility treatments were over, but maybe not my plans for family.

ADOPTION

"Why don't you just adopt?"

Fat Amy: "Don't take this the wrong way: you're the dumbest person alive."
–Pitch Perfect 2

"You're not my real mom," she said sweetly, looking up at me as I pulled the cereal out of the pantry. "I'm not your first mom, but I am real, and I love you," I answered calmly.

We had this conversation regularly, as my daughter worked through her unconventional family tree again and again. Open talks about the meaning of family and parents became part of our vernacular, and our hearts got used to loving around and through the pain of my children's losses.

After we lost our final embryos, my body was done. With each new round of progesterone, my allergic reactions got worse and worse, and I knew I was playing with fire to continue down this road. Even if I could get

pregnant again, my body was such a toxic place for an embryo that it didn't have much chance of survival.

Halfway through our journey with fertility treatments, people starting asking us, "Why don't you just adopt?" We looked into it. Before we started in vitro, I met with a friend who had adopted two children. After we lost our freezer babies, I sent a desperate email to another adoptive mother, asking her about wait times and the process. I had no desire to adopt at the time, but I was gathering options. I wasn't ready. These overtures were my attempt to create a backup plan, a fallback. But an orphaned child isn't a fallback. An orphaned child needs parents who will see her as their first choice. I had to heal my broken heart before I could consider adoption. Once I did, I saw it as the most tremendous gift, not a backup.

After sobbing to my friend months after the loss of our last embryos, she helped me find a therapist and I began the long process of becoming whole again. As the angry red lines and scar tissue on my injection sites began to heal, I turned inward and worked on my broken heart.

People said unhelpful things like, "At least you have one child." Which only made my guilt worse. Guilt for feeling sad at all, guilt because so many people couldn't even have one, guilt because I was too sad to give Elliott the happy mom he deserved.

When people ask me how therapy fixed me, I don't have a clear answer. I don't think there's a magic bullet for healing. It's submitting to the process of letting your feelings work themselves out. It's showing up each week willing to do the soul-searching. It isn't one switch that flips to light up your life, but one small shuffle in the right direction every day.

And then one day after weeks and months I picked up the phone to make another appointment and realized I didn't need to talk

about it anymore. That all my pieces were stitched back together and I was whole again.

We set out as a family of three and a few months later we started the adoption process. It wasn't out of desperation or a broken heart or because we'd run out of biological options, but because we were ridiculously excited about adoption and being a family for a child who needed one.

Maybe that's the difference. Adopt

because a child is in need not because you need a child. No child needs that kind of pressure. Don't adopt to fill a hole. In some ways, you will always be second to the child's family of origin. Of course they'll wish their first family had worked out, that they'd never experienced trauma. You will always be the second choice. A wonderful second plan when their first plan ended, but second nonetheless. Past Me wouldn't want to hear that and Future Me may regret saying it but what can I say? Present Me can be kind of a jerk.

"Just adopt."

Even from our vantage point before adopting, it looked like there was no "just" about it. Like people thought if you couldn't get pregnant you could go down to the Department of Adoptions, take a number, fill out a form, and bang! Baby.

And now as an adoptive parent, I can say there is no "just" about it. Adoption is not a fallback option. It's worth it and amazing and our Plan A now, but having gone through both a crazy lab rat conception and high risk pregnancy *and* international adoptions that hit roadblock after roadblock...the adoptions

grew and stretched me in ways that I didn't know I could bend. I love it. I'm an adoption advocate. But I'm so glad that I didn't pursue adoption as a fallback plan.

Well-meaning friends would advise, "As soon as you adopt, then you'll get pregnant." But believe it or not, adoption is not a method of conception. People say this like it's a wonderful hope, but it devalues the children we're adopting, using them as a means to get the actual "real" biological children. No sir. A world of no.

Do not start the adoption process until you're in a healthy place after going through infertility. In many cases, you hit setbacks and failures in adoption just like you do with infertility. You hit snags and things don't go as planned, you prepare to bring a child into your home only to have the first mom decide to parent or a law change. There are unforeseen obstacles in adoptions that you may never see coming, and you need to be emotionally healthy

enough to focus on what's best for the child. So you have to heal first. After experiencing trauma, a child from a hard place needs a loving family, so we have to be whole.

"She could have kids 'of her own' but chose to adopt instead which makes her extra amazing."

You'll encounter this sentiment about how Fertles who choose to adopt are somehow more noble than people who adopt after infertility. I hear it a lot. I read the book *A Long Journey Home* because as an adoptive parent I think whenever an adoptee offers to share his or her story, I need to listen. And it was incredible. After reading the book, I went to see the movie they made about it, *Lion*, and sobbed by myself in the darkened theater. I loved it, and I also have a bit of a movie star crush on Dev Patel. But one scene in the movie that was hard to watch was when Nicole Kidman as his mother reassured him that she wasn't infertile. That she chose to adopt him and his brother even though she could have children. It was this big moment for his character in the movie and it stabbed me through the heart because this is something I can never tell my kids. Here is yet another way infertile couples are meant to feel lesser and not enough. When we adopt after trying and failing to get pregnant, some people see that as not noble enough.

I call BS. I tell my daughters, "I'm thankful for my infertility because it led me to you." In our family we have all experienced pain and the loss of how we thought our lives were going to go. My daughters thought they'd be growing up in their first families in their countries and cultures of origin. I thought I'd have babies growing in my belly. But we're together now and living an extraordinary life together, with the pain and loss wrapped up amidst the joy and triumph.

If you choose to adopt after experiencing infertility, don't let anyone make you feel inferior because you tried to get pregnant first. Adoption doesn't have to start as Plan A. Plan A can be a journey.

My girls know how much I love them to smithereens, and they know that Mom can't get pregnant. They are not backup kids. They are the kids I get to have because I'm the luckiest mom in the world.

Hanging out together at sportsball practice watching our snarky, sweaty teens, another mom and I talked about parenting. She leaned over to adjust the blanket on her tiny newborn, saying, "You just have to remember what it felt like when your daughter was cute like this. You remember. Think back to those days."

But I couldn't, because we didn't adopt Ana until she was nine. While she's always been cute, she's never been a helpless, cooing baby on our watch, and she came to us with her personality and history firmly in place.

Later that evening, my daughter and I spent a long time talking through school drama and all the teen angst she was feeling, and then she asked me for a hug and I melted in a puddle in the middle of the kitchen.

I've never seen her as a baby, but a hug from a defused teen bomb is something special.

If you're considering adoption maybe your child will be a baby straight from the hospital and you'll experience the scent of a newborn's head. But maybe the child you end up bringing into your home will be unexpectedly older. And maybe the scent from her head is pure sweat and hormones. Maybe both can be devastatingly beautiful.

People ask me all the time which is easier, toddler adoption or older child adoption, and my answer is neither. If you want easy, do not adopt. It's not easy. You think the process is the hard part and it is, but then when you come home and begin suturing together a family, with all the pain and brokenness from past hurts and present wounds, the real work starts and doesn't take breaks.

HEAD SCENTS BY AGE

BABY HEAD:
Powdery clean with hint of milk

GOO GOO GAH —

TEEN HEAD:
Pubescent angsty oil gland

— GAH

"Are they *yours*?" "Which one is your *real* child?" "Are any of them *real* siblings?" "Do you think you'll have more kids *of your own*?" "Do you know anything about their *real* mom?" After feeling on display during infertility treatments, I thought I was ready for the onslaught of rude, invasive questions, but when you adopt, you enter into a lifetime of new ones. And this time, your kids are listening.

I had to heal my own pain before I could withstand being called, "not a real mom." I had to be whole before I could watch attachment challenges tear down any vestige I had of "normality." Adoption doesn't always fill a hole in your heart. Sometimes it creates new ones. It certainly can for our kids.

I don't write these things to dissuade anyone from pursuing this. Far from it. But you need to know the possibilities so you can prepare and search your heart for your reasons. I want you to adopt for the right ones.

My most beautiful and my most painful moments have occurred because of adoption. It's the most important and life-giving work I've ever done. And the hardest.

> My most beautiful and my most painful moments have occurred because of adoption. It's the most important and life-giving work I've ever done.

Made to Order

"Number one or number two?"

"Two."

"Number one or number two?"

"Can I see number one again?"

It's that time of year when I run out of contacts and need to make the obligatory trip to the eye doctor. I wish my trips were more deliberate – like I actively cared about my health – but I suppose showing up is enough for now.

Every time the optometrist swings the phoropter (I had to Google this. Until now I've been calling it the "eye tester thingy") in front of my face and starts A/B testing my eyeballs, I think of my youngest daughter, Evie. It's a weird place to go mentally, but stay with me.

For the longest time, she was obsessed with eyeballs. She'd sing the word under her breath like some sort of Gregorian chant. I'm not sure if this was a meditative activity or an attempt to unhinge her siblings (more likely). But we were careful not to use the E-word around the house for almost a year. Nowadays, she doesn't use the word as much, but she's still enamored with eyeballs and finds new ways to stick her finger into one of our eyes – usually after she's played with lizards in the front yard or touched something sticky.

Like the eye exam, adoption introduces the notion of choice. What age child do you want to adopt? Boy or girl? Country? Ethnicity? Race? Health? You think you're an open person until you're faced with a checklist of what disabilities and diagnoses you feel capable of taking on. It's extremely uncomfortable. I squint through the lenses of my own morality, bias, and fear. I check a box. I leave another blank. I feel like an awful human being because I'm unequipped to adopt a child with severe special needs.

Any sense of nobility I thought I had disappears.

So much of adoption has a "made to order" feeling to it that is hard to swallow. When our oldest child visited us for the first time, we fell in love with her immediately. I think we started filling out adoption paperwork the day after we met her. Even still, the experience felt like we were trying our child on for size. How did she interact with our other kids? Was she the right fit for our family? Would displacing our son as the eldest child be too traumatic? All good questions, but it's hard to escape the eeriness that comes with choosing your children.

My brain may never fully embrace the awkwardness of this process, but every time I hug my girls, I'm certain the choices I made were the right ones.

5 Tips for Adoption

01 **Before starting the adoption process**, make sure you're in a healthy place yourself. Take time to process any grief you're still carrying, work through anger, and give yourself time to heal from the toll of trying to get pregnant. Search your heart and make sure adoption isn't a fallback option, that you're truly ready to give a family and a home to a child in need. Talk extensively with your partner and make sure you're both on the same page about adoption.

02 **Research your options**, from domestic to international adoptions, adopting out of foster care or becoming a foster parent. Research ethical agencies and avoid agencies that have negative reputations.

03 **Spend time with adoptive families and ask questions.** A lot of us are willing to open up and share some of the challenges and joys of adoption, but to protect our kids, we don't just spew everything on the internet for all to see. If you really want to know how things are going behind the adorable photos on Instagram, get to know us and earn our trust.

04 **Look into support networks** and familiarize yourself with resources for adoptive parents, both nationally and locally, like Trust-Based Relational Intervention (TBRI) and Empowered to Connect. Love is important, but love is not all you need. Your child will need more than just your love. You may need other people on your team, people who specialize in early childhood trauma.

05 **If you're considering transracial adoption** (adopting a child of another race), take a look at your community and make sure your child will be able to develop relationships with people who share his race. (eg. If you're a white family and want to adopt a black child, do you live in a community with plenty of black families where he will see himself and be able to identify and develop relationships with people of his race? Will your child be the only black kid in his class at school? If so, you might consider moving to a more diverse community.) Do you have friends of different races? You will need to borrow their lenses to see the world the way your child sees the world and the way the world sees your child. Educate yourself to be the advocate your child deserves.

Well, we have one chapter left. I wish I could end like Oprah, with, "YOU get a baby, and YOU get a baby. EVERYBODY GETS A BABYYY!" But as you know, it doesn't work like that. So to wrap up, let's talk about finding wholeness, no matter what the future holds.

WHOLE–NESS

"It'll happen for you."

Rick Ford: "Nothing kills me. I'm immune to 179 different types of poison. I know because I ingested them all at once when I was deep undercover in an underground poison-ingesting crime ring."
-*Spy*

Last summer, I returned to D.C. for the first time in a decade. It's the city that tried to break me, the city of all my fears and failures. It's not D.C.'s fault. I'm sure it's a great town, but I was going through some stuff while I was there. Returning there, I had stabbing memories of helplessness. I remember feeling so helpless during infertility, and here I was a decade later, walking down a familiar hallway or turning a corner in an old haunt, and the helplessness punched me in the gut.

We drove into town in rainy bumper-to-bumper traffic. Some things never change. My three miracle kids fought in the back of the minivan. Some things do. I spent so many years in this city, devastated by infertility. As we inched our way along I-95 North, I started crying, my kids were fighting, and all of a sudden I was just grateful.

There's a tension that I hold inside my brain. I make no excuses for it. It just is. I have three kids and they are enough and more than I can handle and more than I deserve and I love them more than words can say. And also when someone tells me she got pregnant, I feel a stab of pain that sucks the breath out of me. When I see a mother holding a baby with the ease of two people who coexisted since conception I feel this primal hunger and longing and I have a heightened awareness of my inability to have what she has. Like when someone is eating M&Ms and I didn't want M&Ms and I was fine without M&Ms and then she's eating a handful and I become aware that I don't have any and I have to fight the urge to kick her for no good reason.

I don't want any more kids, and I love our unique road to our beauties, but the longing for pregnancy and that rhythm of creation never quite goes away.

Whether you end up having kids just like you always pictured, have them in a way you never imagined, or find peace without kids in your home, you'll need to find a pathway to wholeness and maintaining that peace, whether that's through faith and religion, relationships with your partner, family, or friends, or finding fulfillment through work or interests. For me, my background of faith makes me feel pressure to say that all my wholeness comes from God, but I think I'd be lying to myself and to you. I spend part of my time finding comfort that this is God's plan, part of my time wondering if God's plan is just something my head made up to make me feel better, and part of my time being mad at God for not explaining it one way or the other. And so my path to wholeness is a super-combo of faith in my God, life-giving relationships with the people in my life, and a passion for my job that helps me feel excited about each day. There is no perfect "one-size-fits-all" wholeness. Wholeness feels different than I thought it would.

People try to reassure you when you're going through month after month of letdowns. "It'll happen for you," they say. It. Might. Not. And maybe you're wrestling with how to survive that and move forward, regardless of the results.

You may have a well-meaning relative tell you, "I just want you to have a family." The thing is, we can't know how all this is going to end. Maybe *poof* you'll get pregnant one day because of a well-timed mojito and Barry White on Spotify. Maybe God will use science to make your baby. Maybe you'll adopt. Or maybe you'll choose to leave a legacy through work or other people's kids or an awesome marriage. I don't know how this'll all play out. But what I do know is that it's possible to be a whole person without a baby. People do it every day.

Sometimes infertility feels forever ago, and then someone announces the Stick

Turned Blue and I'm right back in the emotions, the longing, the feeling left out. It was another lifetime and it was yesterday. A part of me will always be that woman with her face pressed up against the glass looking in on what she can't have. So to the women who are moms in their hearts but not in their homes, the ones with empty wombs feeling the ominous toll of monthly not-yets, I hold you in my heart. I light a candle for the waiting ones.

So to the women who are moms in their hearts but not in their homes, the ones with empty wombs feeling the ominous toll of monthly not-yets, I hold you in my heart.

Maybe the hardest part of infertility is the not knowing. You're reading this and you don't know when or if you'll ever have a baby. If I could tell you that all you have to do is survive two more years and three surgeries, you'd be fine. You'd have a plan to hold onto. But the torture of infertility is that there are no guarantees.

So what does wholeness look like in the middle of the unknown? How do you get up every day and shuffle forward? We don't put our lives on hold. We learn how to shuffle forward while holding our unknowns.

Leaving a legacy

Make plans on the calendar and keep them. Take trips and eat dinners and work your butt off to cultivate a healthy relationship with your partner. Regulate your time spent with your friends with kids. I'm not saying you should ditch them all, but make sure you're also spending time with friends without kids. Develop relationships with a variety of people so you're not

HOW did you become whole?

WHOLE

SKIM

investing all your time into people who have what you wish you could have. Talk about things other than kids. Cultivate that hobby you've dabbled in.

I used my extra time in a couple different ways that have impacted my life. One was writing and one was spending time with other people's teenagers.

Throughout infertility, secondary infertility, and all my adoptions, I wrote and wrote. I wrote comedy sketches and plays and too many blog posts to count. Some of it was good and some of it was the rantings of a weird Christian questioning everything and trying to talk herself into trusting God. Some of it was funny and some of it was horribly cheesy and embarrassing. And at the end of it all, I'm a better writer and have a history of my process through all the hard stuff.

Right after we had Elliott, we agreed to hang out weekly with a group of sixth graders. Alex took the boys and I took the girls. This was through our church, but there are wonderful civic opportunities like Boys and Girls Clubs and Big Brother, Big Sister programs as well. Each week with my girls we'd stare awkwardly at each other and I would try to get them to talk about school and boys and friend drama. I had no idea what I was doing, but I kept at it. I liked that these kids were not babies. I couldn't

picture having any of them as my own children. They were too old to cause my baby-o-meter to twang jealously. They were sweaty and pimply, in awkward stages experimenting with eyeliner and social media. They taught me how to text and later on, how to find emojis on my phone. And I found myself looking forward to seeing them each week.

At the end of the year, we decided to keep going, so we moved into seventh grade with them. Then eighth. Then at the end of middle school, we figured since we'd spent all this time developing trust with these kids that we didn't want to abandon them right when they needed us the most going into high school. I got late night texts on my phone and we unraveled friend drama and boy trouble and fights with their parents.

We spent seven years with these kids and the spring when they all graduated, we drove every weekend to one million graduation parties. During those seven years, we experienced secondary infertility, failed in vitro, long adoption waits, failed adoptions, and expanding from one tiny baby I had to nurse during overnight retreats to three kids.

These teens, other people's teens, helped me feel like I was leaving a legacy and investing in the next generation when my own kids were on shaky ground. My time with them made me grateful that I had the extra bandwidth, made the wait for my own kids a little less harsh.

And as my own kids came into my home, I had no shortage of babysitters. A couple summers ago one of the girls with whom I'd spent those seven years and took on a trip to Uganda when she was in ninth grade ended up taking my own daughter to Uganda. And this year my mailbox filled with another round of graduation announcements...from college. And a couple wedding invitations. Somehow over time our sixth graders are becoming adults starting their own families.

We can leave a legacy, with or without children in our homes.

The ache stays. The ache doesn't go away. Other people's children don't take away the ache. But even in the midst of the pain, we can feel a sense of purpose.

And a little bit of me hates myself for even writing that. I don't want to try to make it right when it's so wrong. Because infertility is wrong. It's broken. It isn't supposed to be that way. And yet, I'd be lying if I said we couldn't also have joy and purpose in the midst of the pain.

So in the middle of your own merry-go-round of waiting, invest in something.

Invest in your relationships, your marriage if you have one, the people around you. Invest in the next generation. Tutor someone or be a listening ear to a lonely teen. Invest in your career or that dream that's just a tickle in the deepest part of your heart.

We can leave a legacy with or without children in our homes.

Don't be afraid to dream. I used to think that I shouldn't get my hopes up because it would hurt too much if it didn't work out, but I've changed my mind. I want to live hopefully. I need to. Like I said before, during that last in vitro that didn't work, I let myself feel hopeful. I let myself dream. I was going to be pregnant. I was going to feel a baby inside of me and maybe make it full term this time. I was going to nurse and apply everything I'd learned the first time around. I dreamed and dreamed.

And when the call came that shattered my dreams, it did hurt worse. I had farther to fall because I'd let myself climb. But I wouldn't have done it any differently,

because the views I saw from the top of my climb were worth the fall. I let myself dream big dreams and my heart remembered how to yearn for joy. I let myself feel wholeness for a moment. It was enough.

After the crash, I laid there for a while, mangled and bruised, and then I started climbing again. And that's what we do. We climb toward hope and we climb and we climb.

Mourn your expectations

After twelve years of climbing I have a unique family of people learning how to hope together. My plans for family have been different than I thought, and the best thing I ever did was mourn the expectations I had for how I thought it would be.

Mourn your expectations. Let yourself grieve how you thought it'd go and who you thought you'd have. Mourn the unicorn children, the ones in your dreams with puppies and rainbows. The unicorn children were never real, but if you don't let yourself mourn them, you won't be able to move on to your real life. Mourning your unicorn kids frees you up to love the ones you actually have, whether they're students you mentor, nieces and nephews, or precious ones in your home who eat food off the floor and talk back to you and borrow your shoes without asking.

I don't know the future. I wish at the end of this book I could hand you a gold medal and a baby. Congratulations, you've won! Here's your baby, start saving for college, and have a nice life!

If only.

Here's what I know. Leaving a legacy is hard. I mean, I sometimes look at the Fertles and wonder if it could possibly be hard for them. I picture them taking Disney trips with their bajillion kids who all get along on family game night after they've enjoyed happy banter over pizza and Cokes.

But then I talk to them and find out that they, too, are struggling and parenting is hard. Leaving a legacy takes a lot of work, no matter how you arrive at it.

So whether you end up having the pregnancy of your dreams, adopt a baby, adopt an older child, volunteer with teens in your community, invest in a marriage that impacts the community around you, or work at your job and help people in your city...it will take hard work and will break you.

I thank infertility for the lessons it has taught me and the ways it's developed my character along the way. Don't get me wrong, I hate it and wouldn't wish it upon anyone, but since we're here, in it, we might as well check out how amazing we are because of it.

The perseverance you've learned in waiting for things that don't come easily will stick by you through everything life can throw at you. You are stronger because of it. You might not feel like a warrior now, sitting in the ashes of your dreams, but you are.

Whenever I have to go through something difficult, I tell people, "Please. I went through in vitro. I can handle it." And I believe that.

ALEX

Stronger Together

Every November, Activision releases its next iteration of *Call of Duty*. (I figured I'd help end this book with a video game analogy. You're welcome.) In the summer, they start revealing trailers for the new game. I drool over my computer as I read reviews and feast on eye-popping graphics. I even drag Melanie over to my screen so she can share in my excitement, but she just stares at me with blank eyes. I carefully walk her through the new features and design enhancements of the game thinking that might help. Nope. She gently smiles and hugs me. She supports me during my moment even though she doesn't fully get it.

As individuals, our struggle with infertility didn't impact us in the same way. Most days, life looked pretty much the same for me. Sadly, I couldn't begin to understand what Melanie was going through even when she attempted to spell it out for me. Half the time, I couldn't find comforting words. I just smiled and hugged her and let her know I was there.

Infertility was the first big challenge we faced as a couple. It can be easy to unload your sadness, frustration, and resentment on your partner – especially when months turn into years, and it feels like you're waiting for your life to begin. But through it all, we managed to grow stronger, hold each other tighter, and come out on the other side a little brighter.

For me personally, I experienced wholeness through my wife's restoration. Not into her former self, but into something new and bold. My wife has always been one of the strongest people I know, but now she's even stronger. And our experience through this process has broadened our worldview and given our lives new meaning. I know the day will come when life crumbles in front of me, but I also know Melanie will be standing with open arms ready to lift me up.

5 Tips for Wholeness

01 **Find an outlet**, some way you interact with the world and leave something of yourself behind. Whether it's a creative endeavor, something you're passionate about in your career, or a relationship that you're building into, cultivate a legacy apart from raising children. When the longing overwhelms you, think over the ways you're leaving an imprint in the world and making a difference.

02 **Get involved in regular, intentional service** in your community. I know you're tired and when I was going through fertility treatments I just wanted to lie down a lot and that's okay. But find something, maybe once a month, where you can invest in your community, whether it's at your place of worship, working with youth, sorting clothes at a donation center, or organizing canned goods for a food bank.

03 **Spend time cultivating the important relationships** in your life. Your close friends, your healthy family members, your partner. Relationships are the most important thing, and whether or not you have children, you have people in your life who need you and love you.

04 **Live a good story.** Your struggle with infertility will be part of your story. What story will you tell? Look for the moments when you're broken but not defeated, the ridiculous moments that made you have to laugh, and the way you rose from the ashes again and again. The best stories have characters we root for, who experience great loss but get back up again, learn about themselves, and ultimately find what they're searching for in the most unexpected way.

05 **Support other couples going through infertility.** Grab a latte and share what you've learned. Laugh and cry together about the hard stuff. Let your experiences shine a light for others on the same path. Helping others feel less alone helps heal your heart.

No matter how your battle with infertility shakes out, I know two things will be true. You will be stronger because of it. Your strength is forged in the waiting, in the tending relationships through the hardest moments of your life. Whether you settle into a quiet rhythm of acceptance, fill out reams of paperwork for adoptions, or give yourself over to the searing cycle of fertility treatments, you will develop the stamina of a triathlete and the perseverance of the most steadfast pilgrim.

You will be stronger, and you will be marked. You will bear the lasting inner scars of infertility. When you see a newborn baby or hear a friend share that she's pregnant, something will happen inside you. It may be different for you than it is for me, but something will happen deep down, whether you admit it or not. You'll feel a twinge. You'll remember your own journey.

What you do with that twinge is up to you. Some people grow bitter or hide or pretend that everything is fine. When I feel the twinge, I acknowledge the feeling, "I feel you, twisty heart, and you feel a little jealous and jaded and snarky." And then I release it and let my own unique road to motherhood rush over the twinge like fresh bubbling water.

I really hate my uterus, but I love my life, and the difficult road to get here makes it all the more triumphant.

We are survivors.

ACKNOWL-EDGMENTS

A big ol' sloppy kiss to my agent, **Kathy Helmers**, who believed in this book even when no one else did.

To my **team of infertile early reader friends**, I wish I could give you a lifetime's supply of ice packs and chocolate. Thanks for your feedback throughout the project, encouraging comments, and ferocity at getting the word out. My wayward ovaries salute you.

To my schweet kids, **Ana**, **Elliott**, and **Evie**, if you accidentally read the sex chapter and never want to look at me and Daddy again, I'm so sorry and I'll keep up the payments for therapy. It's totally my fault for letting you learn how to read. Thanks for being great kids and letting me parent you somewhat successfully.

Alex, thanks for lending your excellent design skills in all your vast acres of free time. You make my illustrations look way better than they actually are. Thanks also for contributing your manly words in each chapter, and for your sperm.

Hey reader, if you're dealing with infertility, I'm your biggest fan and cheering you on.

Also By Melanie Dale

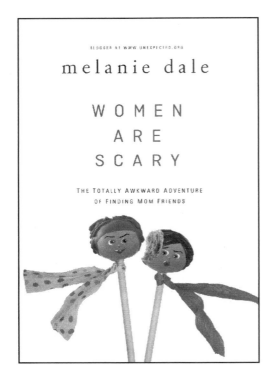

Women Are Scary: The Totally Awkward Adventure of Finding Mom Friends

By Melanie Dale

Published by Harper Collins Zondervan

It's Not Fair: Learning to Love the Life You Didn't Choose

By Melanie Dale

Published by Harper Collins Zondervan

Coming Spring 2020

FROM SIMON & SCHUSTER

CALM THE H*CK DOWN

How to Lighten Up about Parenting from Someone Who Sucks at It

Hey, thanks for reading my book. If something in here helped you or brought you a smile or some solace, then it was worth every second sitting at my laptop and maybe even some shots in the butt. I'm not particularly thrilled that I had to go through infertility, but I am thankful I can share what I learned with you. I know I can't fix this situation for you but if you ever just need to scream into the internet void, I'm here, and you can find me in the places below.

Sloppy Kisses,

Mel

Be my email friend: **unexpected.org/subscribe**
Website: **unexpected.org**
Twitter, Facebook, Instagram: **@unexpectedmel**
Email: **melanie@unexpected.org**
Podcast (iTunes & Stitcher): **Lighten Up with Melanie Dale**
Speaking: **unexpected.org/speaking**

Made in the USA
Middletown, DE
21 February 2020